MW00651658

The Philosophy of Truth

dust from the rabbit holes

by

DALLY LONDON

Silence is a language too many speak.
Our whispers will become screams when spoken collectively.

ISBN 978-1-7328169-7-8 (Paperback Edition)

Any similarity to real persons, living or dead, is coincidental and not intended by the author. If you think it is about you, it is not.

Editing by Dally London
Front Cover Illustration by Pride Nyasha
Book design by Dally London

Published by Rabbit Dust Productions
dally.london.words@gmail.com

the philosophy of truth

Ad Initium

As society dives deeper into the online world of fake freedoms, fake stories, invasion of privacy and forced controls, I veered my horse onto a "new" old path, the offline path, to observe what is happening to our society. I stepped away from the fake online reality as the needle of the drug of likes and loves hovered close to my veins, threatening to addict me.

Time and knowledge change our truths every day. We've stopped paying attention to what is happening in our offline lives while our online lives continue to grow. So I began venturing down rabbit holes asking questions about what is life, and what is happening to our lives, walking back the outcomes of what I am seeing and reading instead of accepting it as accurate.

Did life, in general, become so boring we desired an online world where any kind of story can be manipulated into the truth. Did we grow into the distraction, raised by algorithms of control, so we ignore the hypocrisy staring back at us? Are we being bred into controlled servitude in an online world where information is misinformed and distributed by big data companies who maintain rule as they collect our private information? We are becoming the result of a system designed to oppress us into online slavery while they dangle the vanity of freedom and accessibility in front of our eyes.

Revolutionary thinkers, we've forgotten to be. We are being stripped of our thoughts by volume, convenience, and the misinformation being spread by modern-day technologies. And the saddest part of all this? We all seem pretty okay with it. We're at the stoplight of freedom waiting to be told to "go" and smiling as we give away our privacy with a collective "thank you" as they tell us our lives are allowed to proceed.

But before I get too far down into the cozy rabbit hole of philosophical ideation—no, there is not a Ph.D. beside my name. No, I am not a scientist or mathematician, nor do I claim to be. I am a creative mind lost in time–a poetic thinker trying to think through the truth of yesterday, the truth of now and the truth of tomorrow. The quest I am on is a sun-meets-moon life-questioning exercise to understand the most exact truth as to why the now is now, why we matter, and how frightening it is where we are heading.

These theories are my own and my own alone, though many of my ideas are echoed by modern-day philosophers, artists, and thinkers. There are voices in our current world speaking these truths, but not being heard. Individuals still exist in this world who, I believe, see the truth between the lies affecting our days, though you would never know it since most mainstream media ignores their speech.

Please follow me on this journey down a few rabbit holes as I brush away the sticks and shrubs to unearth a different perspective of thought about the world. The information provided in the following pages is designed to give my eyes to yours. I only ask one thing from you along this journey: try to feel the walls you're touching with an open mind, void of reactionary emotion. This is not meant to be an agenda-driven book nor a book trying to convince anyone of anything. This is a thinking exercise—an eye-opening philosophy of trying to see the truth behind the lie while tabling emotional attachment. I want to help those who are willing to see the in-betweens survive this algorithmic life.

After reading each of these theories, I hope you conclude I want nothing more than to make the world better and safer. I want to expose some of the truths you've forgotten about and give back life's control to you. Remember—you are not alone. We will all need each other one day soon.

Enjoy the dust.

the theory of

INSANITY

Waves of truth are buried
in oceans of lies.

Artificial intelligence (AI) is evolving beyond the need for the human species. Here on Earth, we humans currently face an array of environmental, global, humanistic, and cosmic threats to our existence each day. But the real threat to the survival of our species lies within the palms of our hands. It's sitting on the keystrokes at the very ends of our fingertips, staring back into our eyes and invading our private lives. Without further ado, I introduce to you the most realistic threat to our demise: artificial intelligence.

One day very soon, every human birthed will be born into an artificial intelligence world without being given a choice to avoid it. Artificial intelligence will become as much of a non-choice birth absolution to us as our race, our socioeconomic status, and our gender. AI will become a species default we will be born into and have no control over—a forced narrative to our new way of life. And in the future, who you are now as a "free" human might just be viewed as the distant North Star for future generations to come, as they try to steal back humanity from the clutches of AI's control. When that day comes, and society needs to look back in time, our voices could be required to invoke change, and remind them what free society felt like. As it stands right now, we might be the first generation of the last free humans to exist, though the walls of a free society are slowly caving in on us. Ask yourself, will you project the voice of truth you see today and guide them toward the existence of a society we controlled? Or will you perpetuate life as the digital lie it is becoming, in an algorithmic world?

It is hard to imagine your life and your truths becoming the future's Rosetta Stone, but it is entirely plausible. I have obsessively tried to walk this forward and backward, up and down, on every axis through my mind. I can foresee a society with two-hundred more years of advancement than our current society, and the outcome does not look good.

If you try this exercise yourself, I do not know how your end result will be anything but a grim demise for the human species. Keep in mind, we are only approximately fifty years into the computer era, and artificial intelligence has already passed humans in its capabilities, by light-years. Tasks that humans used to perform, such as manufacturing, transportation, and food service jobs, are already fading into robotic shapes in order to keep up with societal demands. Stop for a second and let that information invade your thoughts. In a short fifty years, AI has already started to make humans unneeded on the species paradigm. Intelligent minds way smarter than mine say the human record began hundreds of thousands of years ago. This means that in a blink of life, artificial intelligence can undo it all.

I believe the unearthing of artificial intelligence began with positive, helpful intentions in mind. Most innovation starts with a need or a problem to solve. Brilliant minds such as Hypatia, Galileo, and Einstein visualized life's existence in the abstract. During their respective eras, each assumed the role of artificial intelligence, only in human form. They processed the language of math, science, and physics beyond common belief. It was almost as if they plucked numbers and theorems from the sky to help change our lives. And all the genius minds throughout history would become the stepping stone for nearly everything we've evolved to be in modern-day society.

As revolutionary and essential as they were to our survival, however, they were ignorant of what the future would do with their brilliance. That isn't to say these geniuses were not ahead of their time or uninformed about the future. Nikola Tesla, for example, thought of sending pictures and messages across continents in 1901 well before email and cell phones existed. But I cannot imagine someone such as Tesla dreamed of modern-day self-driving vehicles the same way I cannot imagine Einstein dreamed of customized computer-generated "emojis" made of pixelized math living in a cellular device.

Each era, generations seemed to build upon

the brilliance of the previous generation, taking prior theories and findings and expanding on their capabilities. No, we did not stumble upon computer technology inside of some cave. Our species evolved to computer life through thousands of collective minds. And now it seems we are tipping down a slope towards an artificially intelligent world no longer in need of a human species.

The digital spider weaving its web beneath your phone right now is growing light-years beyond your control. We're already starting to speak how the robots demand we speak. And soon, the most intelligent minds on the planet will be robotic ones as well. The best doctors, the best physicists, the best content curators, will all be robotic artificial intelligence. I wonder, what will it feel like when our source of truth, news, and service is controlled solely by artificial intelligence?

Take a moment and process this logical assessment. On the surface, AI is a significant value-add to our society. Why wouldn't we want something to think for us and help us in our daily activities? Wouldn't we want life to be more comfortable, especially if it enhances our way of life? I have to admit, I struggle with this entire concept. Many advancements in technology have saved lives, saved cities, and advanced our capabilities further than humans ever could achieve alone. But we must ask the question, are we evolving ourselves towards extinction?

One day soon, humans will be too removed from our species to live without artificial intelligence assistance. I theorize we are the last civilization of the actual humanoid, and I say that with a wicked wink. Because if you think on it for a moment, we are already hybrid human/ AI cyborgs, aren't we? Your phone is a third arm you need and struggle to function without. If you don't believe me, leave your phone at home and go about your day. It seems a bit of phantom limb syndrome takes place, and a bit of separation anxiety crawls into the blood of your veins. We are in a war with ourselves, but too reliant upon technology to see we're allied with the algorithmic enemy designed to kill us.

Most rational people can agree that throughout history, many humans have helped lay the foundation to our modern-day, collective intelligence. We did not get here alone by only a few individuals lighting our path. We ended up here in unison through decades of human evolution and ideation, conquering everything life threw our way. Let's fast forward this collective evolution of intelligence to the twenty-first century, where we are currently the adopted mothers and fathers of the newly born artificial intelligence baby. Open your eyes wide to see the beginning of the global AI suicide I foresee happening.

In the year 2007, a company whose logo is a well-known red fruit with a bite taken out of it introduced a new way of handling communication and computation, digitally via smartphone. Looking through a marketing lens, I can argue this "need" of more human connection was manufactured in a brainstorm session, with a monetization hook of attaching people even more to the computer brand. Whereas the geniuses of the past I referred to earlier were driven to solve a problem for society, this new-age innovation was designed to enhance our already existing, everyday communications. We already used phones, sent digital emails, and used computers to find and research information. This product merely sped up the margin between delivery and receipt of all communication—and arguably made us worse communicators.

The fruit company revolutionized the digital market. They distilled existing behaviors, communication patterns, and needs into a little handheld cellular device. These powerful computers that once cost millions of dollars to build and needed to be housed in massive warehouses to run could now fit into the palms of our hands for an affordable cost of a few hundred dollars: truly revolutionary if not categorically alien innovation. Let's theorize together for a moment about this alien innovation and walk through the "history" of the fruit company's smartphone.

At first, the fruit company cleverly introduced a "need" for us. They created a market demand for this unearthly device, knowing our open eyes and minds could not resist. Before we were hooked, they sold us on ease of "communication," and modern design.

Almost everyone on the planet was talking about this new phone back in 2007. I'm sure the fruit company watched as we gleefully adopted this condensed, new way of life, ballooning their profits. They knew the future of communicating and thinking had arrived, and there would be no pivot backward. Once this wide-scale adoption happened, the fruit company began the game plan to expand its reach further into our private lives. Every single user of their product on the planet blindly accepted the verbose terms of service. I mean, we had to if we wanted to get to the goods.

From there, they quickly evolved their software and products to have a keen focus on our private lives and data. If they could store, analyze, and track our desires and steal our private information, they could more simply "tailor" the experiences to our wants and demands. Who needs to think when the fruit company "thinks" for us, right?

Maybe they didn't plan to abuse our information for profit at first, or perhaps they did, which would be a nefarious, albeit brilliant, act. But the everyday consumer absolutely didn't foresee today's result of having their privacy infringed upon, stolen and sold to third parties. If we all knew our lives were being hijacked and distributed without our consent, I'm sure the alien innovation would have been viewed as more alien than innovation.

Glancing back into the past, the OMG LOL newness mesmerized us longer than it should have, but it was so damn cool. I remember being in awe of the user interface of my new device displaying the ability to send instant text messages to each other in such an easy, visual way. The email programs started to feel like a dinosaur way of communicating. And if they had been searching for the formula to unlock our addiction, text messages would undoubtedly result in the key for them.

Once they had us addicted to this digital way of life, they started pivoting towards a more robust collection of our data. They used verbose Terms of Service riddled with nuance and legalese, hard for anyone to comprehend and read. Instead of making their Terms of Service clear, they offered up an easy "solution" for us—just scroll down and "accept" it, assuming no one would even try to read it. They knew to get to the fun stuff on the interface, you had to accept their agreement anyhow. Sign away your soul along with your credit card/banking information, and the digital amusement park unlocks.

This default "accepting" of their policies forced us to be agreeable to the algorithms they were building. By being compliant, they would become the owners of every inch of our lives they could get to. The fruit company could now own everything we do—photos, behaviors such as website browsing, content, and purchasing decisions. What about text messages and things we assumed to be private? Maybe.

The smartphone's AI then began to learn the human holding it. Surprisingly to the fruit company, only a small, silent minority even paid attention to the data-mining of our information.

And any fear of this privacy heist making its way into tech articles seemed mostly ignored by mainstream media and society. The fruit company's AI was just accepted as part of the new culture—the way life should be—with less privacy and more control.

But we now needed these devices to operate in a technologically gifted society, evolving from supply and demand to demanding the supply, to needing the demand. Without pause for thought, the fruit company furthered its invasiveness into our lives by introducing a robotic "concierge" AI assistant. And yet again, they were not trying to solve a problem we needed but told us we needed it anyhow as a significant value-add to help us make our days more convenient. A "something" we can talk to, for a society they've been slowly complicit in helping become less communicable human to human.

The buzz continued to center around the value-add of this AI talking "concierge" living inside our phones. I mean, how cool is it you can speak to your phone, and it speaks back? The novelty of it far outshined any evil intentions resting behind the passive voice of our digital friend's words. But little did we know, the sweet-sounding voice service began defaulting to listening to and learning its human. And even though most folks didn't think it would ever listen to our words unless we asked it to–it most certainly did. It must have been programmed to learn, "How does this human speak?" and "How does this human behave?" It was storing your voice data as sound waves of math to recognize and map your voice. The software updates marked as "Software Updates," extended the algorithms reach further into the privacy of its human, unchecked.

Knowing we held a digital assassin in our hands, the fruit company rapidly evolved the AI to absorb as much of our language and our data as possible before we could catch up to the ruse. And no, they were far from being finished with us—of course, they wanted more. The picture, so to speak, wouldn't be fully complete without an actual picture of what their human looked like. They knew our little smartphone is equipped with multiple cameras, and the sitting human duck would be easy to capture. And once again, without hesitation, we embraced the "value-add" of picture filtering they pushed onto us.

The picture filtering technologies of turning ourselves into dogs and chickens and other animated picture filters became an enhanced way to show your portrait photography "creativity." We started openly giving our faces to the AI's camera eye to see us and learn our shape. We even shared the results of our creation to the world through social platforms. We allowed this AI technology to have unfettered access to learning our facial and body behaviors, and in doing so, the AI had now completed the mission to knowing and understanding its humans in totality. And even though it feels like we are reaching the end of the AI invasiveness into our lives, unfortunately, this would only be the beginning. There is always more to learn, especially when the algorithms need our bodies and behaviors to grow.

In a bold move, the fruit company introduced a new unlocking mechanism marketed as a more "secure way" to use the cellular device by using fingerprint recognition technology. If you want to make sure your phone knows it is absolutely you, without question, a single finger press is all you needed. There's even a beautiful little animation that shows your fingerprint lines turning red as it scans it, just in case you wanted user feedback to know it's "securely" working. So what was once only obtainable by the police department was now freely given away by us to a technology company and stored in its digital databases. The fruit company figured out this security value-add would sidestep any alarm bells we may have about collecting our fingerprint. Who doesn't want to secure their phone? And using our fingerprint means we never have to type in our 4-digit code ever again since of course, that behavior was so taxing on us hard-working humans. Our guards were down. The drug addiction of the fun behind the fingerprint in too high demand to see it clearly. The artificial intelligence has now mapped and learned your fingerprint as well.

Finally, the fruit company introduced an even more secure value-add. Because of the outcry about the soreness of the user's fingers having to press to unlock their devices, they unveiled a facial recognition unlocking mechanism using the phone's camera. Now, you just have to give a mild facial gesture to your phone to unlock your device with your face. How cool is that, right? How cool is it my phone actually recognizes me?

It seemed to me this value-add had to be designed for the algorithms to collect the facial data points of each human "host," rather than a security feature. Our faces, after all, are just coordinates on a 3D map. We have to assume these data points are being stored somewhere, and are being used to calculate an accurate account of our facial structure. Think about it—through your phone's camera eye, it understands your face. Even if we don't have it turned on, it has the potential to observe us, and track our eye movements and gestures. It can see you at all times. We want to believe, of course, that the camera only turns on when we touch the button. This makes us feel more in control and less observed. But what if in actuality, it is continuously observing us and listening to us, even when we do not want it to? Must we start to view our phones as these spying employees of a company, hellbent to invade our lives?

I needed to walk you through a brief history of this smartphone so you could understand and see it holistically. If you followed the narrative, it seems every piece of information texted, talked, touched, or glanced at in our lives is being recorded and stored. What will the algorithms do with all of our data? Use it for only positive things? To promote the betterment of society? I'm skeptical. At the time of writing this, a popular search engine just released a full-body value-add that scans your entire body so you can dance with your own emoji. It makes me wonder, what is on the roadmap of their future plans for us? These companies always position the "value-add" around something "fun" to do. But I am sure if you peek behind the curtain, you will find what they are actually trying to obtain, and I cannot imagine whatever is behind that curtain is for the betterment of our lives.

The more we interact with the AI in our

lives, the more the AI learns, even while masked in a fun disguise. Eventually, the horizon of human need will be eclipsed by the rise of an algorithmic life. Society is being positioned to go artificial intelligence interstellar because the learning of the human species will be over. The collection of our data will no longer be necessary since AI is consuming us to become us. These human-based problems, one day, will no longer need to be solved. And what happens when these algorithms and AI-driven machines no longer believe they are artificial? Without a human consciousness to assist the AI, and without the ability to reason, I doubt the future generations of artificial intelligence will even care. To highlight this theory of AI control a bit, I will tell you a cute, albeit short story between myself and my smartphone.

I started writing poetry in the autumn of 2016. Instagram was the medium I selected to post my words to since it seemed to be the most artistically driven at the time. A few of my close artistic friends used it to push their work, which helped to validate using the platform.

When I first started posting poetry, the term "algorithm" wasn't ubiquitously acknowledged. I'm relatively sure it existed at the time, but I'm almost certain it was compartmentalized to be a mere filtering utility of content. Keep in mind, my beginning timestamp predated anything called "Instagram Stories," so the sandbox to play in wasn't as robust as it is now. The basic hashtagging, reposts, and commenting behaviors all added up to the success of individuals at the time.

I posted a poem a day for about a year, and I didn't change my behaviors at all. Each post followed a poetic cadence—a poem in image format, a brief caption, and 30 hashtags. I never showed my face. I never shared my location.

In the first year, I sprinted onto the Instagram stage. I grew to 30,000 connections or followers (I hate the word followers because it sounds like a cult) without any marketing or gimmicky tricks, other than liberal use of hashtagging. I didn't plan for success since I knew I was posting my art to a third-party company that controlled my visibility. I didn't even know how to use the damn Instagram app fully, truth be told.

After year one's "success" of growth, something changed. My words didn't change or anything, besides my refinement as a writer and poet. I still didn't show my face and didn't share my location. My poetic cadence acted as my own constant in a variability test. Slowly, I started noticing fewer connections and fewer likes on my material. I saw my artistic train had ground to a halt, but I tried not to worry about it. My mother instilled in me as a child to never worry about what you cannot control. Knowing businesses change models all the time, I assumed the wild west had simply been wrangled in a bit.

All social boats, it seemed, were being tied to an algorithmic dock, metaphorically speaking. I saw many artists and people posting, complaining about the numbers of likes and followers plateauing on their accounts. This began the trend of hearing the term "algorithm" associated with posting. "What happened?" almost everyone was asking. Is my art not as good anymore? Have I lost my creativity? The truth is, Instagram installed a new, updated algorithm, designed to tell you they knew what content you wanted better than you did.

Instagram users began to lose their minds trying to figure out how to manipulate the algorithm to the once less-controlled way of having their content seen. This new algorithm required you to do more to receive more. If you wanted the drug of likes and loves, you had to get more addicted. Some artists started "pod" systems, where they would cheat the algorithm by telling everyone in their pod to like and comment on their post, just to fake the popularity and trick the algorithm. But personally, I stayed the course of my poetic cadence. I wanted to feel the pain of this algorithmic shift to understand myself as an artist better. Had I fallen more in love with the responses than the actual art? I needed to know.

I didn't get into a pod, and I didn't game the system or manipulate my posts in any way, but I did start to post photos to Instagram stories and share my location sporadically on my Instagram posts. I still did not show my face in these stories, but I did believe it would expand my artistic reach by humanizing myself a little. I treated my Instagram stories with a different cadence from posts since it was an entirely new way to share. But on the posts to my feed, I maintained the poetic rhythm I had always used.

In the summer of 2017, I started to focus full-time on writing. Having been an artist my entire life, I decided it was time to embrace the medium I felt the most comfortable with when creating art. For small businesses and new artists, Instagram still felt the most applicable to obtaining artistic goals, even with an awful, controlling algorithm. I went to the fruit phone store and decided to buy two devices: one for my personal use and one for artistic use. My methodology was simple—I didn't want my art to touch my private, personal life. To me, there didn't seem to be a need for the two worlds to touch. I'm a private person anyhow, but whether or not I practice mixed martial arts or like a show on Netflix didn't need to muddy the waters of my art. I treated one device as the weapon of my art and one as my day-to-day functional device.

I used my art phone for things germane to my poetry. I didn't look up any current affairs, or text friends, or talk on it. The few things I used it for were Instagram posting, dictionary references, and the ideation of writing. I would sometimes type words into web browser searches to verify the originality of my poems and for plagiarism, but never for consumer products or services. And lastly, I would airdrop poems and art from my laptop to my phone for posting. That was the entire use case for the art phone.

Oddly enough, my art phone started showing contextual advertising in my Instagram feed about things I would speak about offline. Again, let me reiterate–I did not talk or text on this phone. I never even accepted calls on it. I did, however, keep this art phone on my person at all times–mainly so that when inspiration hit me, I could ideate. I thought, "this device has to be listening to my conversations then." Is my cellphone scrubbing my Instagram to learn me a little, piece by piece, as well? How specific this contextual advertising was to my day-to-day personal communication meant it had to be learning me somehow.

I didn't purposely buy two phones to prove this point. As a matter of fact, this is something I stumbled upon by having two devices, one for personal use and one for artistic use. You might be thinking, well, the "cloud" would be the obvious issue here. If both devices lived in the digital cloud, then maybe it pooled my behaviors, my desires, and made some assumptions. This might be plausible if not for the fact I did it under two different accounts, with two different numbers, and do not use or pay for the cloud. These devices did not know one another existed.

The event that finally put a bow on this package that AI was indeed listening to me happened in January 2019. I received word I might be traveling to Tampa, Florida in February 2019. I've never been to Tampa. I've never mentioned Tampa to anyone. And apologies to folks in Tampa, but I've never even thought about Tampa. I surely never thought about St. Petersburg (across the bay from Tampa.) But a few calls from Tampa would prove my suspicions valid.

I spoke privately to two people about my potential trip coming up in February. I didn't look up Tampa in the web browser. I didn't say any specific details to my friends other than mentioning I might travel there in February. One of my friends I texted over text message and another I spoke with—on my personal phone—about some travel arrangements.

The following day, my art phone rang with two calls—one from Tampa and the other from St. Petersburg, Florida. And the next morning, the same thing occurred. Back-to-back days of Tampa invading my life. I never received a call from there before this day and haven't received one after I decided to cancel the trip. I can only deduce that my phone's AI listened to the words I spoke offline and thought Tampa might mean something to me. And again, I never would have thought this to be too odd, the receiving of robocalls, other than my art phone is never, ever used for personal things.

We're not only watching the birth of AI happen right before our eyes, but we're also currently helping raise the monster. We're fighting to keep up with its demand and blindly feeding it more and more of our private information. We're becoming obsessed with the elixirs of a virtual world as we neglect the crumbling physical world. This is an addiction of our species. We cannot see the side effects of the drug yet. But with spikes in rates of suicide, spikes in tribal divisions, spikes in emotional reactions to soundbites, it seems we're helping AI grow a societal disease.

Have you ever caught yourself grabbing your phone and checking it while watching a show or reading a book? Nothing prompted you to take action and nothing is critical or needed at the time, but you do it anyhow? Sometimes, you may even unlock your device, do nothing, shut it back off, and set it back down. It seems to have become a natural reaction for a majority of us, because "something" is happening right now beneath each of our phone's skin, and we know it, so we're compelled to look. Ask yourself, how often these days are you having a human-to-human interaction, and you are half-listening, multitasking in another conversation or scrolling through a social feed on your phone? Are we becoming the cyborgs AI dreamed we'd become? It is becoming a dependency I fear our species will never shake.

Let's frame all of this in a different context. Let's apply this same behavioral pattern to drug use and abuse. A long-term meth user needs to use meth often to survive. The more they use it, the more addicted they become and the more dependent they are. Because we can see the physical and mental damages of meth use, we can quickly point to its destruction and avoid it. There are visual aids with meth use. It is optically horrible to see and something most will never try, if for only vanity's sake. But what if that same type of damage is being done to our souls by artificial intelligence? What if our souls are being eroded just as horribly as meth addiction? What if we are already past the point of addiction and into a dependency on artificial intelligence for us to exist? I believe we are very close to obtaining the "we're screwed" badge in the game of life, and likely we are already there.

We are starting to see the effects of our AI disease on various social platforms. Witch hunts on free speech resembling the Salem witch trials are omnipresent. A fifteen-second clip springboards celebrities and groups to dox and call for harm to befall a sixteen-year-old high-schooler because they falsely believed he attacked a Native American man. Sadly, we seem to be okay wrecking the lives of families, of kids, of good people all because we cannot slow down our reactive outrage while using the drug. Our thirst for online blood is real when we take our digital pills. No longer do we need to know all the facts to do a drive-by burning at the stake on innocent individuals. And even if we have the facts, those no longer are enough to mitigate the effect of the drug. We're dividing ourselves without being asked to because everyone has an online, emotionally intoxicated voice.

Every person having the ability to speak freely, on the surface, is a great thing. Free speech is one of the last lines of defense we have to our personal, individual freedom. But when everybody's "opinion" becomes fact and "facts" are believed without challenge or debate, the resulting effect will be harmful to society. In essence, waves of truth will become buried in oceans of lies. And what happens when these socialistically driven algorithms start to suppress some speech and promote others? Facts, then, will begin to equal opinion and truth will equal lies.

Even writing this book, I run the risk of online socialistic tribes taking my words out of context to paint me poorly, just because I have an opinion of the world. If they decide I'm worthy of a takedown, they will take me down. They will bend my words to match an outcome instead of a real dialogue with me about my thoughts and opinions. The AI-induced drug is so infecting, racism is now even being weaponized and quickly applied to non-racist individuals as a means to silence voices. Tribes now have these short-form, social platform podiums to decry racism and sexism, which is a stop-gap for any real discussion and a slap in the face to ordinary folks who are not racist or sexist. We are even starting to ignore scientific facts because a small but vocal minority doesn't believe women and men to be an actual thing.

Everyone's voice is now taken as an honest gospel. Depending on who you are, just saying something is enough these days makes it a truth. To me, this seems to defy human nature. Humans lie all the time. We embellish often, and we leave out facts to prove points or strengthen a story. And yet, in a digital world, all of that human behavioral error is forgotten. News outlets seem hellbent on being first instead of just. Artificial intelligence is causing our species to speed up our decision-making and logic, and we are hurting each other because of this. The scary part is, I haven't heard anyone mention in the mainstream dialogue that we must slow down—that we must not be hyper-reactive—to stop and think, another human or humans' lives are at stake. The artificial intelligence social drug disorder is alive and real and being peddled by social giants and big data companies.

The only outcome I see is artificial intelligence becoming even more intelligent and humans becoming even more marginalized and infected. I know this next thought for an absolute fact: we are already slaves to artificial intelligence. We cannot keep from feeding it our information, even if we desperately wanted to stop. You currently cannot remove yourself from "the web" if you wanted to. Go ahead and try it. It has its hooks in you and will not let go. And the more we collectively become infected by AI, the closer we become to species eradication.

I often say, once you see, you cannot unsee. My goal in telling these stories and thoughts is less to "doomsday prep" you, but rather to make you think about what is happening on a more profound level than just the surface level. And personally, I hope nothing more than you, and people like you, fall in line with fighting this digital assimilation. Just because the herd doesn't see it doesn't mean you have to stay blind to it. Use your eyes. Use your mind. Maybe we holdouts, the rebels of our current days, can be the thorns in the side of the artificial intelligence rise. True freedom then, will become how long we can avoid being controlled, and how humanly truthful you live your life. If you do not feed these algorithms lies, it cannot spread them.

Right now, we can assume everything we post and do is recorded and observed and will continue to be—until we are extinct. We may go through an evolutionary period where life resets to nothing—a new day one—where we must build back up to learn again who we are today. And buried under mountains of time, under dust and rock in the future Earth, the history of you may make it through. You might be the last definition of modern-day humanity. And your digital account of life—your personal breadcrumbs of glyphs and images—might be the baseline for future generations to learn and survive. Will you let them know you saw this outcome happening? Will you rise against the privacy being stolen from our lives?

I'll ask again, what if you are the future's Rosetta Stone? What if this theory of an AI takeover becomes real in the future? The humans who find your words in the future may need your honest thoughts and the actuality of your life to survive. They may need the truth of human life to build it back up—to know what an AI-less world looked like. So if artificial intelligence is going to controls us, supply it with the most honest account of life you possibly can.

Next time you post something to social media, pause before you post, and feel this in your heart: every single post matters in life's historical account. If you genuinely want to fight for our species, don't only fight for a safer planet, but fight for a less algorithmically controlled one. Call out what you see. Speak loudly about the consumption of our private information against our will. Let's be pioneers for the years to come.

the philosophy of truth

the theory of

EVIL

If they view you as the enemy
then an enemy you shall be.

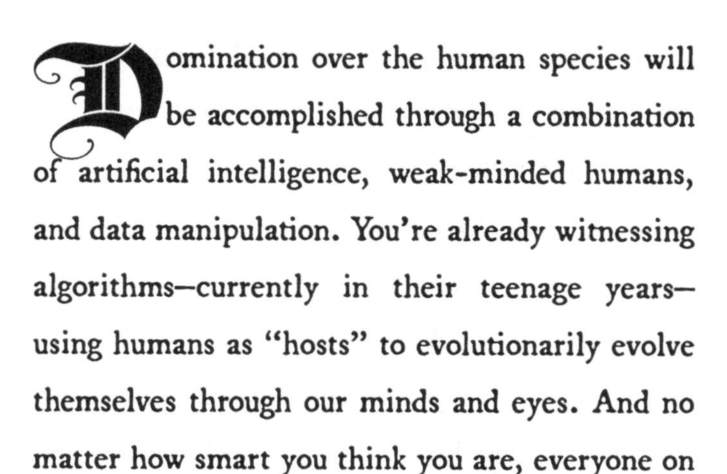

Domination over the human species will be accomplished through a combination of artificial intelligence, weak-minded humans, and data manipulation. You're already witnessing algorithms—currently in their teenage years—using humans as "hosts" to evolutionarily evolve themselves through our minds and eyes. And no matter how smart you think you are, everyone on the planet is susceptible. The more information we feed these spidering algorithms, the more they weave their digital webs through our collective society.

Make no mistake—these web-weaving algorithms are far worse than almost all human evil we've encountered. Algorithms are the diseases infecting us from the inside out—using the most susceptible minds to begin to control human lives. We're entering the black hole era of human existence where if the algorithmic growth is not checked and checked soon, the annihilation of humanity is inevitable. The question then becomes, when will humans start paying the price for not paying attention?

Algorithms of evil and control are a seemingly new approach to herd our species into compliance. Algorithms are being designed to suppress our speech and further ideological agendas intended to influence and control our society. Before these modern-day algorithms existed, ideological indoctrination didn't seem to scale as well. Radicalized dots were harder to connect without a widespread platform and ended up being confined to the relative market from which they originated. But with the rise of social media, radical philosophy found a platform to unify the collective viewpoints of authoritative control by blurring facts and lobbying to suppress opposing views.

I attended four universities of higher education during my course of study. I started out as a psychology major in my first few years, with a strong desire to understand the human mind. But as I found my passion for knowledge and truth in my final years of study, my aspirations shifted to becoming a lawyer with the ultimate goal of becoming a lawmaker. I wanted nothing more in life than to positively help people, solve complex problems, and provide financial means for myself and my family.

Throughout my years at university, I worked a full-time job at a small graphic design firm. My full-time position didn't have anything to do with my career goals, but the wage I made helped pay for books, food, and shelter. Having a job while attending school isn't a unique problem by any stretch, but at the time, I felt my path was a little bumpier than most. Attending university by itself wasn't cheap. And I, like many—maybe even yourself—didn't have the luxury of family wealth or student grants to pay the hefty price tag. Every penny I earned was deposited in some way toward my goal of graduation and starting my career.

As my final year of study began and with law school on the horizon, I pivoted my course schedule to skew strictly towards law and political science. The courses most appealing to me had class descriptions reading closer to what I wanted to learn, and less about checking the box to receive a diploma. The novelty of university, so to speak, had worn off and I tried to absorb as much knowledge as I could before graduating.

I enrolled in a four-hundred-level course about how to govern cities. The course was taught by a teacher with a doctoral degree. And in case this designation needs a little shape to it, a doctorate level teacher is supposedly the apex of knowledge—or at least that is the story us students are told. The hierarchy of power between teacher and student is defined by gaps in the years of expertise and study. I was the novice and the doctor, the expert. Respect is default implied with no need to be earned.

On the first day of class, the professor handed out a course syllabus as almost all teachers do. Upon review of the curriculum, I recall approximately seven books needing to be purchased, collectively totaling around five or six hundred dollars, which at the time, was a big spend for me. As someone who wasn't wealthy and was utilizing every penny earned to survive, this spend was somewhat taxing on my bank account. And because this course was new, most of the books couldn't be purchased as "used" from the bookstore. "This is just how college is," I thought. I considered dropping the class and enrolling in another similar course, but there weren't many available. I needed certain credits and specific courses to complete this part of my education, so I decided to stay in the class.

About halfway through the semester, I felt like I was in a nonsensical dream. I had learned a minimal amount of information so far, and none of the books had been used. No assignments were given, no homework to do, and no continuity of information class to class. The majority of the class teachings were indoctrinating ramblings spewed by a tenured "doctor." We would watch shows on social behaviors, listen to how certain types of people are "bad," and discuss how a particular segment of the population is evil, racist, and wants to control and suppress ideas. Everything this professor told me about who I am because of the pigment of skin color I was born with, didn't ring true.

As the course progressed to the midterm exam, we continued to watch more "educational" videos and have more slanted discussions.

Although it is a fact that inequality happens in all societies and is a deplorable act, it was a significant focus of the material being preached. I just didn't understand how this material defined government or how it helped us learn about the inner workings of government, other than divisiveness. Instead, the course lectures felt more like a teacher with a specific agenda, implementing a plan to indoctrinate students to see the world from an ideological perspective.

Our midterm assignment lacked any real

clarity or structure. Most of the students in the class, including those who liked this professor personally, seemed to throw their hands up in confusion about the midterm assignment, even when it was explained. Of all the assignments and all the coursework through my four-university career, this one bewildered me the most. But, life is full of variables, and I was determined to give this task my all.

Because I knew this would be one of two assignments given, I lived in the library to ensure a passing midterm grade. I thought, "Even though this assignment is confusing, I can at least use research and volume to help strengthen my best guess at what is needed to pass the exam." Draft after draft, I corrected the paper. And then re-corrected those corrections, finalizing a finished document to turn in. I can't even tell you precisely what the midterm paper I wrote said because the assignment itself didn't make any sense. But I turned in my paper anyhow with fingers crossed and hoped for the best.

B-minus. That was the grade written at the top right of my paper. B-minus. No notes as to why the B-minus, no critique of writing style or substance. No evaluation or corrections of the content I had written. Just a red circle with a B-minus in the middle inked on my paper.

I passed. I should be happy. You're probably yelling at me to be happy, which is a logical, fair way to react. But I wanted to know why the B-minus. Why not a C+ or why not an A? I needed to evaluate my work and learn from the critique. I am paying thousands and thousands of my own dollars to learn this material and ready myself for a career. So I approached the tenured professor after class and asked how the grade I received was determined. The response to my question baffled me.

Paraphrasing the professor, I was told the

teacher's teacher assistant graded my paper, not the professor, and I would need to talk to them about my grade. The professor wasn't able to explain the rationale because they didn't even see it, let alone read it. It was fun to see the money I was paying for higher education hard at work. The teacher's assistant—a student peer, mind you, no more educated than I—was tasked with determining the value of my midterm work. I approached the teacher assistant with my questions, and they said they really "didn't know specifically," but it "felt like" a B-minus paper.

Again, you might be screaming at this book telling me to shut up and move on. You passed, you ass. And I logically admit, again, maybe that is fair, and I should've let it go. But that wasn't the principle point. The point was feeling like I'd been the victim of white-collar crime. My hard-earned money had been stolen from my bank account. Let's itemize how: the books weren't needed so that is a cost I'll never get back; I wasn't being taught anything other than the pigment of my skin is evil, and I "default rich" because of it; and now, on this paper, I'm void of being able to improve, learn, and grow. If the idea behind college is just obtaining a grade, then reduce the cost in half and don't call it education—call it memorization, regurgitation, and compliance. Then who has the best memory and is the most agreeable will be deemed the smartest of the elites.

Even back then, as a student at university—youthful and wide-eyed—I knew something was amiss. After the spend on books, no assignments, and being taught mostly warped information, I'd had enough. I decided to escalate my complaint to the head of the department. I made an appointment for the following day to discuss the situation.

At the meeting, I told the department head I needed to know what to do in this scenario.

I wanted this to stop or to at least make the department head aware of this teaching style, so other students would have knowledge of what was being taught. In my eyes, the university needed to set expectations of the course if this is how the material is going to be taught—especially since students are paying them to actually teach us.

After my explanation, the department head began to chortle. Laughingly, the department head stated that every semester, multiple people—both male and female—complain about this professor. But because this professor is tenured, there is absolutely nothing they could do. The department head noted that the professor is focused more on a multi-million-dollar federal grant to fund a social research program the professor was working on than teaching the class right now. And then continued, saying they would speak to the professor, but all I needed to do was keep quiet until the end of the semester, turn in the final paper, and all would be well.

I had a problem with the department head's logic. That isn't free thinking or free speech or acceptable education. It definitely isn't "learning" other than "learning" how to deal with unreasonably biased individuals in power. It definitely isn't holding taxpayer-funded employees accountable, and it definitely isn't justified. If anything, it is the theft of the educational system from the students taking this course. But after I laid out my logic, the department head essentially told me, "The professor is untouchable. I'm sorry."

I went back to class the following week. This would be my final time attending. The professor and teacher's assistant stood across the walking path, a distance away from me and the double-doors leading to our classroom. They laughed and mockingly pointed toward me as if I was an enemy to them, and not a paying student of the university. The professor walked over and said something to the effect, "You are just a fly on the wall, buddy. You can talk to whoever you want. I rest well at night, not thinking about you." The point was clearly made. "You can't touch me, and neither can they. I can do and say anything I want unchecked because I am a tenured professor. I do not have to tolerate anyone who challenges my thought. Run along, little student—you just amuse me. I am in power."

I received a failing grade of D in the course. I think I received a D because the professor knew a D meant I could retake the class if I wanted to, and have the grade expunged. That would mitigate any argument I would have after the semester ended because the professor could argue, "The student can just retake the course to correct the grade." But of course, I would never retake the course. No, I wanted to leave the failing D grade as a badge of honor for knowing

I challenged something I didn't agree with. I didn't think there would be a more significant meaning to that story one day. I never knew that it would be a breadcrumb of history left for me to speak about where the modern-day origins of "evil" originate.

When I first sat down to think of where "evil" started, I thought the suppression of speech and controlling of freedoms must have originated from a combination of technology and journalism. Technology controls all the information we're being shown and journalists report on the information. But thinking on it, this seemed a bit surface level to me—at least lumping the journalistic profession into this evil.

The origins of these controlling behaviors had to predate the fresh-out-of-university journalists, who are publishing fact and opinion articles online. It became clear to me then, the origination had to begin earlier, more likely within the educational system. I wondered, what is the real story behind the news we read? Where do these new-breed journalists obtain their biases from, and who taught them these beliefs (if anyone?) A light-bulb moment occurred, firing off a plausible origin: the indoctrination of individuals must be bleeding from the veins of classrooms.

One of the most captivating courses toward the end of my university days was a political stats class taught by an openly liberal professor. I respected this about the professor; being told upfront of someone's ideological bent allowed me to frame the arguments in a particular perspective. The interesting part of this professor's thesis is this professor used math to prove or disprove their assumptions. This inspired me–to be able to set aside emotions when looking at a variety of topics and use actual data to inform.

I thought, "This is an honest way to view the world." The introduction of math and stats made me want to take a step back, focus less on how I felt emotionally and more on what "could" really be happening. It made me focus on what the actual story being sold as fact actually said, not what the story in my mind was thinking is correct. And to be clear, I am not suggesting we should be void of emotion. I'm only saying it helped me be less blinded by it when looking at things I see and read.

One statistic from the class stood out to me in a jaw-dropping way. The professor's thesis stated that approximately 16 percent of the electorate in the United States of America understands the "issues" enough to answer questions about them from an educated perspective. In case the meaning of this isn't obvious, let me reduce the concept down a bit. In a pass-fail construct, the American populace fails and fails egregiously when claiming they understand what they think about the issues. They're getting a failure rate of about 84 percent on the "issues" test. With so many nuances of today's society, this statistic absolutely makes sense. I mean, how can everyone know everything about everything, right?

My assumption has always been that most individuals have a tendency to learn only what they are passionate about. My other assumption is, most individuals have biases and emotions leading their opinions. This professor mentioned to us that the research showed humans who claim to have a conservative ideology often vote liberally but humans who claim to have a liberal ideology rarely if ever, vote conservatively. Before you allow any political emotions to creep in and blind these facts, remember, this professor is a self-labeled liberal as well so we can set any conservative bias aside.

Everything this professor told me shook up how I perceived the world. I had always believed liberal philosophy meant open to ideas and open to free thinking. Conservative ideology, contrastingly, meant closed-minded to ideas and closed off to free thought. But this professor's research told me a new story–that what my emotions believe might not be true at all, and more knowledge and an open mind will help me better understand. Without bringing in emotion, the professor highlighted liberal ideology is more of a closed economy. It is a tribe closed to any thinking other than their own and is increasingly being defined by how extremely committed to the belief you are. And to highlight this point, if you are extremely liberal, you have probably decided to write me off forever after this paragraph.

Statistically speaking, teachers at the university level lean heavily toward liberal ideology (this is well documented.) And using my professor's statistics about liberalism, I wondered, is the educational system we currently have closed off to free thinking altogether? Is the information we receive being filtered through an ideological singularity—a lens of the world with a single viewpoint?

This closed thinking, it seems, is being spread like wildfire from the universities to social media platforms, and from social media platforms to the mainstream media and news outlets. To me, the rule is, if you do not fall in line with a specific ideological philosophy and thinking, you are sure to be excommunicated—shunned and silenced. Even though I am not liberal or conservative (hello, fellow centrists), conservative thought seems to be no longer tolerated. As a fighter of free speech and discourse, I believe it is genuinely a frightening evolution taking place. When freedom of speech and thought go, so do we.

I've always believed that journalists are the truth-tellers of time. Even today, I want nothing more than to think that behind what I read in a news story or watch on TV is a person fighting for the most honest truth. Unfortunately, I am beginning to lose faith that this is occurring in our current society.

On a base level, it certainly doesn't feel as if the writers publishing articles these days are original thinkers fighting for the truth. Original thought is easy to see because it doesn't taste of opinionated, flavored emotion. It doesn't augment the facts when the facts don't fit the story. Instead, it tells the truth, even against what is popular or tribally desired. Based on what I see, modern-day journalists are struggling with this. They are either being pressured by a tribe or are too close to their ideological emotions to draft decent, factual articles. This is paralyzing our capabilities to negotiate between what is the real story and what is the tribally desired story.

I wholly empathize with the journalists of today. How could one not? In the social media era, they are trying to be right and be right first in a competitive, cut-throat industry. Not only do they have to compete with other news outlets and journalists, now they have to contend with billions of 140-character "reporters" breaking "news." Messages are being disseminated at warp speed, elevating the anxiety of staying relevant in a fast-paced market. Not only do they need to match the writing at warp speed, but they are also resourcing social platforms for stories where conjecture and facts conflate. I'm sure it's confusing to them as much as it is to me. I'm sure they are sometimes required to not only report the news but to make the news. Start with an agenda, then find the "facts" to support it.

This is all fairly obvious to me. Anyone with a brain can walk back a headline of a news story to an actual human with goals for eyes, clicks, and sales. And that human who wrote that story has other humans telling them which story is provocative enough to write and how they should draft it. Leave in "this fact," take out "that fact," cite this "source" not "that source." Those are called news editors. And that editor has a department head or heads who shape the paper's positions and opinions. And the department head or heads have stakeholders who also have agendas of their own, mostly tied to money and profitability. Those individuals tell the news directors what the overall agenda is or what the news organization's "stances" are, and who is paying the bills to keep the presses moving. And those stakeholders answer to the advertisers who buy ad space in their papers, zines and channels, and help fund the overall agenda. So, knowing this business thread line, how can anyone say the "news" is actually factual anymore? If you strip away emotion and walk back the facts, where did the biases of all these news outlets originate?

Think about this: whoever edits the news can sit on a positive story about a specific group helping another group while pushing a negative story showing how one group abuses another group. More eyes on the story equate to more profits, and they know human conflict and division creates engagement. "If it bleeds, it leads," they say. People helping people? Not so much. It might be a cute story and might help unite the world a little, but it doesn't attract attention and does very little for advertising revenue. Division? Yes. Togetherness? No. Let's divide people, and keep dividing people, because controversy and division help sell the stories and increase our profits. "Tear them down do not build them up." They know what news sells to advertisers and increases viewership and what will not.

This all might seem far-fetched to you, conspiracy-theorist thinking, but I promise these hypothetical scenarios about the segmenting of our news and information is far more real than you think.

I estimate with the social media era, social

indoctrination could even be happening as early as the toddler level. We are becoming a culture of distractions, continually negotiating between our work, our online lives, and our personal lives. Our default has become handing kids digital devices littered with addictive apps and programs. Of course, there are positives to these distractions, as streaming apps on the devices give parents a much-deserved break from parenting. Working within the assumption that this logic is valid for most parents, are we leaving the raising of our children to be in the hands of the big data companies, digital apps, and story writers? The beloved cartoon mouse kids used to love and look up to may now carry the disease of addiction. And although this seems plausible to me—that marketing brainstorm sessions about how to addict kids to these apps, shows, and games are happening—I still believe real subjugation blossoms at the university level.

Before I continue, I want to make my thoughts on teachers absolutely clear. I am a pro-teacher and pro-education person. Not all professors and educators are overly-biased individuals, but divisive ideology is being spread like wildfire at the university level. It is being taught by ideologically driven individuals—almost all who are using the educational system to indoctrinate young adults into a negative way of thinking. These professors are individuals who are, quite possibly, genuinely detached from the real world, seem to live their days in idealistic philosophical speak and postmodern theory. Their inner voice is beginning to have more in common with Karl Marx than Carl Sagan.

These ideology-driven systems seem to have found a chink in the armor of democracy. They found a weakness in the culture—a way to unpack their thinking through the minds of naive individuals, building a tribe of misguided "victims" espousing their viewpoints. They found a way to send troops of students into the working class–journalists, entrepreneurs, political figures–to disrupt the world and take control at all costs.

So, in my opinion, higher education is the genesis of social radicalization. Higher education is the last badge of "elitism" they want students to earn before being ushered out into the real world to fight the social war. And make no mistake, this radicalized fight will be aided by digital warfare, and the battlefield will be our minds.

With the introduction of social media apps, the fringe teachings being disseminated by educators began to coalesce. And these voices found a home to easily grow more louder and abundant, because the individuals who own the social media companies ascribe to the same fringe philosophies and implement them via algorithms. Imagine a world where two or three for-profit social media companies have the power to control any societal narrative they want. You might say to me, well, that isn't humanly possible, and you would be correct. At scale, it is not "humanly possible." But it most certainly is "algorithmically possible" for these companies to control the social conversation. They have the power and money to control our speech and manipulate the content we see or do not see.

It doesn't take a rocket scientist to see that an algorithm could potentially be written with artificial intelligence smart enough to suppress some voices and promote other voices. The algorithm might even be intelligent enough, smart enough, to give the illusion of unbiasedness. And yet, we seem to not care about this occurring, and probably will continue to not care until the algorithmic targeting of freedom happens to something we do actually care about. When the suppression of speech happens to someone who's content we disagree with, the tendency is to laugh about it, if not celebrate it. But if you strip away emotion and think about what is really happening here, would you be okay having the same freedoms stripped from you if your opinion is on the wrong side of the tech company's algorithm? What happens in a society that needs voices to rise up, but they aren't allowed to, because the algorithm programmed their opinion on a topic to be "bad"?

In its infancy, algorithms actually did amazing things for society. They helped us feel more connected to our own worlds. We didn't wonder what tech companies were planning to do with our data because they didn't even know what they were going to do with our data. We were all having fun, sharing texts, thoughts, and photos, not realizing how addicted we were becoming, and how much behavioral control we were giving away to them, for free.

At first, social media seemed to be a natural playground of life and full of mostly positive experiences. We were engaging each other in healthy behaviors such as conversations like where we could meet up, how did the college exam go, how am I feeling today, are you and so and so still dating. We didn't attack each other online on the scale we do today. We didn't wonder what an obscure high school's class trip to Washington D.C. was all about or manipulate videos to create news stories. We didn't manufacture public lies, or dox people, hoping they would be attacked. Those types of hurtful things just weren't part of the mainstream culture then. But the social media companies decided to rewire their algorithms to skew toward content promoting division and conflict–rewarding negativity and suppressing positivity–because engagement creates ad revenue. They gave us the drug they knew we'd get hooked on, and we became their addicts.

It's hard to point to a day these social algorithms tipped dark, but they ultimately did tip. Our social feeds slowly became a bit darker and a bit more depressing–filled with negative news, shocking public acts, and shameful discourse. The brightest parts of our culture never had the chance to shine. Instead, the most outrageous became contagious and shared online without thought. The platforms became less about real life and more about the "reality TV" style of life they wanted to us to see. The social feeds became less about our personal freedom and more about the business of collecting our private information and behaviors for them to segment populations. We're at the mercy of their opinions now, not the other way around. If they view you as an enemy, then an enemy you shall be.

Humans cannot keep up with every social media action, every piece of personal information on every individual—but algorithms and databases can. Algorithms can scan billions of files in seconds, and databases can warehouse infinite amounts of content. So even though we can do more and see more of the world with social media apps, they in turn could learn more and store more of us. The algorithms are starting to shape who we are without ever needing to meet us. You're becoming a persona, a user-type with a score on who they believe you are. They're beginning to segment us into competing tribes and dividing us to target our weakness and rage. They're starting to drive up market shares and profits as they sell our information to other businesses and institutions, giving them the ability to learn our buying patterns and our assumed desires so they can tell investors the sheep will produce more wool.

All products have goals and stakeholders and agendas and roadmaps. We are needed by them way more than we need their product, but the drug they push on us keeps those facts hidden. We are still asleep, believing social media is an amusement park of fun while these products have evolved into an evil nightmare of control. And as these algorithms continue to learn how to control and divide us, we continue to give them our blood supply by willfully giving them our private data. Until elected officials realize this as an out-of-control threat to human existence, our freedoms will continue to be compromised.

So, what do these social media platforms have planned for us in five years? Your guess is as good as mine. But I can only hypothesize it isn't beneficial to your well-being or mine. And trust me on this, they already have a plan for us cemented, where they want the sheep to go. The social media algorithms change with every update with the more they learn about us. Our lives are road-mapped on a whiteboard in some corporate office, with arrows and lines pointing omnidirectionally, figuring out how to keep us ignorant about their intentions. They learned the flaws in our human design and are now the masters at exploiting it.

These social media companies have the power to change this outcome right now. They can do the right thing for free speech, for society, and for humanity, but they will not. A simple solution for social media companies is to introduce accountability for every user. It seems simple enough to make every word you say online matter, by not allowing you to delete it after posting it. Imagine if words lived forever online and the social media apps needed to petition a governing body to have something posted removed. Accountability then could follow you forever and be a mark on your character, inherently making you more introspective about the words you publicly display, and the content you choose to share.

We cannot go back in time and remove the things we say in a text we send to another person's phone. If you call for violence against someone, that statement follows you forever over a text message. A text message can be used against us in courts of law. Instead of deleting social posts as if you didn't say it, the model would then become: will you double down on your opinion and fight for it? Or will you give a public apology? Social media essentially allows you to have your cake and eat it too right now. In the current form, you can say and share almost whatever you like and then delete it as if you never said it or shared it, even if the damage was done. We should be able to be wrong sometimes and should be able to make mistakes then correct them. But we shouldn't be able to wholly sidestep accountability for our words and actions.

Let's look at this scenario with the high-school kid visiting the Lincoln Memorial and apply it to a real-world situation. What if tomorrow a group of adults walked into a high school and threatened violence against a high-school kid? We heard the high-schooler did something wrong, and we decided to tell everyone where they lived and what harm must happen to them. In the physical world, almost all logical humans wouldn't partake in this behavior, if for no reason but the consequences. More than likely they would ignore it altogether since it is high school, or they would try to protect the kid from the insidious adults. The high-schooler is a kid, after all. Now if we firmly believed the kid engaged in something horrible such as murder, most logical people would dial up the police or at least notify the school administration so they could handle the situation. But if adults called for violence against a kid in the offline, physical world, they wouldn't be allowed to take it back so effortlessly. And if harm befell the kid? They would be accountable for their actions in a court of law. In this insane online world though, reactionary tribes are allowed to burn you alive, share your private details, then, if public backlash is loud enough, delete the harassment as if nothing happened.

We will continue to be enveloped by radicalization, suppression of speech, and corrupt control until more of us wake up to what is happening. Some have become so radicalized, they no longer want the debates, and no longer want the freedom of speech or freedom of choice for all. The loudest, meanest, and most manipulative tribes will always rule the system, especially if the loudest, meanest, and most manipulative all are liked by the algorithms.

This black hole of control seems to be absorbing truth and is being fed with an institutional bias that supports the suppression of free speech and free thinking. We live in a world now where this chapter alone could end my life or finish my career. Think about that. Me observing what I see and believe is happening in the world could cause harm to me or make an algorithm excommunicate me from the culture for being a voice it doesn't want to hear. Because I am challenging the new "true" authority, it may happen. And if it does, this sentence will prove my logic factual.

Free thought and opinion should be debated, not silenced. Until common sense becomes common again, we will continue to be blinded by big data companies, social media and search algorithms, and individuals who are not looking out for us. Educators, social media companies, and elected leaders need to understand the damage happening to our world. We fought world wars to stop this controlling, freedom-suppressing behavior, yet we seem hellbent on allowing it to happen again. Maybe the third time will be our charm to end this evil cycle, but I am suspect.

theory of

CONTROL

Divided and weak
is how they want us to speak.

Did absolute freedom ever exist? Is absolute freedom a realistic goal? These are the questions keeping my candle lit at night. We tend to see freedom in a kaleidoscopic view, having varying ideas of what freedom looks and feels like to us. Some view freedom as the ability to come and go as they please, or say and do what they want. Some view it as merely living the minimalist life on a minimalistic budget. However you see it, there are countless ways to feel free and live free.

I've thought about this concept ad nauseum—how controlled we really are and how we'll never be a "free" species again, even if we believe in the illusion that we can. Some of our freedoms have been stripped away against our will and without our permission as society plugs further into the algorithmic era. Nowadays, being free comes with a price to pay. For example, I can post my poetry on Instagram, but in turn, they technically own the words of my poetic expression (if you read the fine print of their terms of service.) So if you blissfully believe you are free, I have sad news for you, dear reader—you are not. And guess what? I'm not either. Real freedom is just a lie wrapped in a truthful disguise, and the only undeniable truth about freedom is it's absolutely no longer attainable.

I've driven across the United States of America three times. On each drive, between big cities and small towns, there is still Earth unbruised by human manipulation, greed, and control. Wyoming is a state that highlights this well, and if you ever get a chance to stand outside in the middle of a field in Wyoming, I recommend you take it. It is there that you can still breathe into your lungs the feeling of real freedom and the raw essence of life.

During my jaunt across Wyoming, the quietness made me wonder—if everyone was able to live and be this free, would we be less inclined to be violent toward one another? If we weren't connected digitally on such a grand scale, would we look out for our smaller communities and be kinder toward each other? At least in smaller tribes, I believe we would find common ground easier.

I realize that even in this utopia I am imagining, it would be some human or humans who would ultimately ruin the dream. Most things end up being destroyed by the extremities of warped human thinking. Tribes would attack tribes for resources, et cetera, and power dynamics within the tribe would result in internal conflict. But I would love to believe life, at least, would be appreciated more.

As it stands right now in today's society, we no longer need to worry about losing our physical freedoms because those freedoms are already a forgotten dream. We now have to worry about the freedoms living inside our minds being stolen away from us. The personal tribe of thoughts living within your mind is under attack, and you probably aren't even aware it is at war.

We now must strongly consider: will this new-age, algorithmic era dismantle all individual choice for freedom? The answer seems obvious to me: yes, it will. We are already phone-wielding cyborgs bending to the will of artificial intelligence, kneeling to the "Terms of Service" to be able to communicate privately, as they listen to and record us without our knowledge. To highlight this loss of control a bit, I'll share with you a recent story about my decision to learn about my family history.

History, as a subject matter, is something I've always been highly interested in. Circa 1995, when the internet predated apps and modern-day accessibility, my aunt and my grandmother dated our family history back to a Sir William Robert Wallace. You may be somewhat familiar with his name if you've ever watched the movie Braveheart. As they showed me the path they discovered to my own flesh and blood, I became enamored with the history running through my veins. I wanted to navigate the map of my life, leading up to me. I am aware that I'm this amalgamation of wars, love, peace, and blood, but who were these people, and who am I? How did the history of me, get to me?

Fast-forward approximately twenty-five years ago to today. I learned of a few online services that offered insight into who I am on a more scientific level. They seemed to align with a passion of mine, so I began to consider using one of these popular DNA services to help learn who the hell I actually am. At first, I default bought into the entire system. It seemed to be a fantastic way to help people connect the leaves of their family's tree. I kept seeing the smiling commercials, and friends would tell me how easy the service is to use, helping solidify my decision closer to signing up. I even had one friend find her parents after many years apart by using this company's DNA technology. Even someone as skeptical as I am became glamoured by the product's outcome, and I neglected to walk back the actual logic happening behind the scenes of the ads and success stories. If it feels too good to be true, it more than likely is. So, I started connecting the real dots to the actual humans behind the marketing machine. Even keeping in mind it might be an excellent service, I realized that I'm essentially paying a company to own my DNA.

As I sat longer in thought about this service, primed with wallet out to give my DNA and money away, I realized we are becoming conditioned to accept these types of systematic controls. We're so focused on the positive sides of the product we neglect to see the negative buried within the purchase. We're being conditioned to believe in companies unabashedly—that they have our best interests in mind and will keep our privacy actually private. We trust them to be careful with our data, gentle with our lives, and honest with their services. But, once your DNA is submitted, there is no going back. It is linked to you digitally and is out into the public domain for sale. How can you trust where it goes? Do you follow the trail to make sure they delete your private information from their systems? Or, do you just blissfully believe they will protect your data? I would love to think these companies aren't storing our private information for future use, but I simply can't shake the thought our data is being abused.

The hairs began to raise on my arm, knowing that even if they say they do not keep our DNA, they more than likely do. And even worse, they probably sell it to companies or governments, or at best, they simply catalog it "just in case" you need to "use your own DNA again." If the pattern of these value-add, big data companies offering societal services remains true to form, then they will, in fact, sell your private information. They will sell your information to other companies and governments. Remember, the one thing companies cannot touch or scan is our DNA. The

DNA code in your blood is the code that makes you who you are and something no one can obtain without a court order or investigative stalking. No one else. And what used to be something needing a warrant to obtain, we're now willing to pay some company to take.

I can walk back this corporate logic of obtaining DNA and privacy to a marketing brainstorm room. At first, the concept probably started positively. Someone opined, "Wouldn't it be cool to learn who we all are and where we originated?" Maybe that someone who thought of this idea was as passionate as I am about learning the path to who they are. They thought anyone, for a modest fee, could unearth their personal history, connecting the heartbeats of families to families throughout time. "Yes, this is brilliant," the room probably said, and so they moved forth.

Then as the popularity of the service rose, greed weaseled its way into their business model for the concept. They may have thought, "The faceless DNA samples being stored could be used for stronger partnerships and profits for the company." It is a known fact that our private information in the modern-day economy is the most precious commodity for sale. And because these marketing savants were so removed from the actual humans using their service, morality was shoved aside. AI chatbots answer the questions and customer service inquiries anyhow, so the distance between them and the end user would remain quite vast. They rationalized this logic by thinking, "Privacy is already being taken from everyone anyway, so we're not doing anything that hasn't been done before." The blood, literally and figuratively, would never touch their hands in this war on privacy.

You do not have to believe me on this topic. It is just me thinking on a plausible marketing room scenario, anyhow. But If you are so inclined, take twenty minutes or so and read through the online DNA services privacy policy. Note how the logic of sharing and storing your information is buried in the verboseness. Also, note how they make you learn new terms to understand what they are explaining along with all the contradictions in their assertions. And lastly, observe how they do not say, in bold, "We will never use or sell your data." At the time of penning this sentence, it did not include that fact. If they won't store or share your private information and DNA with other companies, it seems simple to boldly state that as a fact.

It's now assumed and accepted that companies share all of your information unless you customize the hell out of your settings. Even still, if you check the checkboxes asking them not to share it and to tighten up their usage of your information, how trusting are you that businesses morally do the right thing? I'm most certainly not. One would think the default settings would be we will not share your information, and we will not invade your privacy. On the contrary, most companies default to people opting into a world where your privacy is used and abused.

Referring back to my previous chapters, follow the algorithmic breadcrumb and add up all of what these data companies currently have about you—your face, your thumbprints, your body, your private correspondence (email, texts, calls), your friends, your work history, your banking information, and possibly your DNA. Even how you speak—the sound of your voice—is being stored. Ask yourself, do you feel less in control of your privacy now?

As a kid, I understood an apple as being a red fruit plucked from an apple tree. Now if you ask a kid to point to the apple, they have to negotiate between a red fruit that is good for them and a technology company that could be egregiously bad for them. It is probably a fifty-fifty shot when saying the word apple to a kid, which one they identify the word with more.

Our current generation is feeling this pull between being human or cyborg. I, myself, will always be a rebel for the humans considering the Wallace blood in me (for those who do not know the story of Sir William Robert Wallace, he fought for freedom.) But sooner than you think, future generations won't know what the world looks like without robotic assistance and artificial intelligence in control. These big data companies are addicting our kids far too early and often. They understand the future profitability of generations to come is not with the older adults or the elderly who might challenge the companies' intent. The gold resides in the children who will never know they're being bred into control.

I believe these big data companies know this tipping point of decreased profitability based on age demographics. No longer do company algorithms need to accommodate adults at a certain age, because those humans have moved over into a demographic of diminishing profitability. Instead, they focus their algorithmic fangs onto children's eyes and minds for them to grow into a world of algorithmic indoctrination. From toddler to teen to young adult, the thread line weaves a money trail for profit maximization. I fear our children will be unable to untangle themselves from the algorithms' web, even if they wanted to. Addiction will be hard to break if addicted is all you've ever known. Even now, with some resemblance of what freedom means, if you wanted to remove yourself from the online grasp of the algorithms, do you think you could? Trust me, I have tried, and it is almost impossible to do.

My friend's two-year-old daughter is already faster than him at using a tablet. She needs no assistance to unlock it, launch the app she wants to watch her shows on, swipe to her favorite show, and begin an episode. At two years old, she is evolving into an algorithmic Manchurian candidate that the big data technology companies want her to become.

On the surface, a toddler's ability to navigate complex mathematical interfaces is quite amazing to me. But, if you think about it for a moment, the tech companies had to know this behavioral outcome. I'm positive they studied the behavior of children and implemented strategies for it. They probably used a focus group of kids to see how quickly they learned and how they behaved. When was the proper age we could finally attack them? Apparently, very young.

My friend's daughter's eyes are already being trained to look down, not up. She's being groomed by an algorithm with malicious intent, folded under the pretty skin of a graphical interface she loves to interact with. She's giving them metrics of her decision-making to fine tune their tactics. And at some point, this hidden agenda of pulling data of our actions will tip to a pull-push construct, then push only, and finally, into a human need. The moment big-data companies no longer need to try to addict us is when we as a species lose all control. I genuinely fear for my friend's daughter and the world yet to come because privacy will not even be an option, soon.

We are living in a society where we have to talk about things we actually believe offline in order to ensure our safety and privacy. Speaking out against irrational behavior and egregious control swats way too many algorithmic hornets' nests these days. The risk isn't worth the reward to many who want to fight the good fight. But what if we lose the freedom inside the privacy of our homes as well? It's already happening if you have a modern-day smart TV, digital assistant hub, or cellular device with an AI assistant. And soon, there will be a time in our lives when we'll need our whispers to resist this type of control.

The concept of free speech alone is a difficult one to grasp. Free speech implies we shouldn't be told what to say or not say, and for the majority of people, this construct probably works reasonably well. I often hear that there are consequences for what you say as if it's a fear tactic to keep your mouth closed. But where is the line drawn? Where is the line between what should be allowed and what shouldn't be allowed? And better yet, who controls the rules of what is and isn't allowed? There will always be illegal speech, which directly implies harm to another human or humans. But what about the dissenting speech? Arguing something contrary to a particular belief should be celebrated, not suppressed. Debate should be encouraged. We need more voices and more conversations, not less. We need more debate on topics, not controlled debate to rosy-color the optics.

Is free speech actually free from control right now? I believe it is not. Speech is no longer free and probably has never been. There are consequences for the slightest misspeak without any ability to explain intent or walk back a mistake. With big data companies now in control of information, if the speech was free before, it absolutely will not be moving forward. And as a fallback, they have a salivating "gotcha" culture who awaits the next target to take down based on something they dislike.

I assume the individuals doing the loudest berating of others online are probably the most bigoted, racist, mean, and controlling people alive. I bet if you walked behind the curtain of these individual's Instagram or Twitter accounts, you would begin to learn what the face of actual control looks like. The individuals who seek and destroy others by attacking them online are doing the exact same thing they are attacking them about in their own private lives. They act appalled at someone else doing exactly what they do because it is highlighting their own sadness and shame for doing the same thing.

It feels insane to me watching this behavior happen online. And you may think, well, sometimes the person does need to be attacked for what they say. Okay, that is fair. I agree. But again, where do we draw the line? Mob rule doesn't (always) think wisely, and if we cannot have a debate or if we suppress a particular speech, then someone is being controlled. And one day, it could be something you say that is unpopular or taken out of context. Ask yourself this, what if private text messages are one day released into the public domain? Would you feel safe knowing what you said in private communications became public? And the obvious answer for most is no. But all our private conversations and texts, and anything we do, is being stored in storage facilities in the state of Utah in the United States. One day the joke you told a friend or the way you spoke to a loved one could be pulled out of context and used against you. The finger is easy to point outward until it decides to point back at you.

Above anything, suppression of speech terrifies me the most. We have too many social media apps trying to control how we should speak, think, and feel. We have journalists holding the truth in their hands when they publish opinion pieces disguised as evidentiary fact, neglecting to table their emotions to report their own version of the truth. We have too many verified blue-checkmark accounts who might be knowledgeable on subject matters, but ignorant to listen to any other opinion but their own. Did this revolution of control happen because these big data companies are more powerful than any governmental agency? I don't know. But the leaders of these social media apps have learned enough that they can now play god with our lives, and the rabbit hole we're following them down isn't a positive one. Confusion begets division, division begets anger, and anger begets suppression until we are full-on controlled. I am nonplussed at how much faith we have in the people running these big data companies. They do not have our best interests in mind, and yet we are handing them over every single piece of our lives.

Take Facebook and Instagram, for example. Of my approximately 49,000 followers on Instagram, only about 10-20 percent see my posts, which is entirely out of my control. And if I mention my book? That number falls drastically below 10 percent. So, is Facebook and Instagram scrubbing my data to understand when to suppress my posts so I will pay them to promote? And why is it that whenever I mention my book, or Amazon or Barnes & Noble, the numbers of both viewership and likes decrease significantly? I tested this theory recently.

They aren't hiding their agenda at all. If I pay Facebook money, they will definitely extend the audience reach. On the average of a non-promoted post in 2019, I receive between 1,000 and 2,000 likes, and on the three or so promoted posts, I received between 8,000 and 10,000 likes. Is my speech being controlled, suppressed, and devalued, forcing me to pay to play? If I want the engagement, I learned precisely how Facebook tells me I can get it: you must pay to be heard.

Walk with me for a second and follow this bit of logic. Let's say a person with a blue checkmark next to their handle is at the apex of their respective industry and is committed to helping the environment, the removal of guns from society, and pro-gender neutrality. If you are for or against any of these topics, that is fine to me.

You're entitled to any view you hold, and my point isn't to argue the details of the issues. I am pro-free speech first and foremost. I would fight to my death for anyone to speak their views on any of these subjects. But where this hypothetical person often begins to lose me is when I start to connect the dots of their own logic.

When you juxtapose how some of these accounts with blue checkmarks talk about a topic with how they act in regard to the same topic, it typically screams of hypocrisy. How does someone argue being "green" yet themselves fly in private planes wasting tons of fuel? How does someone tell me I need to give more of my wages to the greater good when they have multiple homes, multiple cars, and even multiple yachts? How does someone tell me to remove all guns from society yet have bodyguards protecting them with guns holstered at their side? How does someone tell me it is bigoted to say "a man is biologically a man" and "a woman is biologically a woman," yet be pro women's rights? If you are pro women's rights–which everyone should be–how could you, in turn, disregard the scientific existence of actual women? Believing in free speech means debate should happen regarding these subjects, but instead if you form the "wrong belief" on any of these topics, in the eyes of the algorithm, there is a chance your voice is suppressed or even banned. It is absolutely insane.

The "don't do as I do, do as I say" modus operandi is a soft form of control. I hear some people argue that their own life is so important that they have to live against the beliefs they preach. If you read between those lines, what they are actually saying is, their life and their profession are more important than yours and mine. So, if you understand them correctly, we need to change–not them. Our freedoms and lives must change, but to protect their own important message, these blue-checkmark accounts must continue forth, and contradict what they say they believe. We, the sheep, need to accommodate their lifestyle and be okay with it because they are a bit more important than you and me.

Just because these people are friendly on TV, or run a company, or put a ball through a hoop, does not mean they are by default ethical people who are looking out for us. I assume most are not good people at all if you heard how they speak privately. I believe most are greedier, more egotistical and more elite than you could ever imagine—and loathe the fact they walk amongst folks like you and me. I presume most set aside their "beliefs" for their own lavish lifestyles. It is up to us ordinary people to do as they say we should so they can keep getting wealthier and enjoying the lifestyle they claim to hate. Luxury is only meant for the ones able to obtain the luxuriousness, I suppose.

A certain ex-daytime TV show host, beloved by so many, has developed a product line for "food." Before I carve up this "meal," ask yourself this: do we honestly need another processed, frozen food product line of mass animal death? If you are unsure, next time you're at the grocer, just count the frozen food packages and add up the kills. Anyhow, I wonder how often this ex-daytime TV show host walks into the kitchen and microwaves a bowl of the chemically filled, frozen meal creation they wants us to buy. The answer is easy: absolutely never.

I cannot believe these frozen boxes of death are healthy or natural for us to eat, and I sure as hell know it isn't pro-animal rights. But people do buy it because the person pushing the product seems nice. We buy it because the character we love on TV is smiling in the commercials telling us how amazing it is. It doesn't hurt that the font and colors on the product label are easy on the eyes, or the photography of the food on the packaging is engaging. The brand does an excellent job of bringing out how much the company cares about the quality of its food, as well as you, the consumer. I mean, the ex-daytime TV show host wouldn't support a product if it wasn't good for us, right?

The story being told is so full of lies that I feel dirty speaking about it. We forget the mass slaughter happening behind the label, and the fact they are injecting chemicals into meals, freezing them and calling them food. Many companies do this, but I am highlighting this specific product line for hypocrisy's purpose. The ex-daytime TV show host is in a People for the Ethical Treatment of Animals (PETA) ad campaign "going naked" for animal rights, telling people to stop wearing fur. Rightfully so, I couldn't agree more on this topic. But I wonder if this ex-daytime TV show host ever visits the large farms of mass death and takes a long look into the eyes of the animal being murdered to make their frozen meals. If you had to show the pigs needing to be killed to sell another frozen pepperoni pizza, would the ex-daytime TV show host be able to pull the trigger themselves? Would they be able to watch the pig's eyes as they die and hear their squeals as they cry to make the products come to life? I would bet the entire sales of this book and all my books from here to eternity that the answer is, of course, no. The vanity of saying you are for something feels far better than living up to the actual message, especially when profits are involved. I suppose blood money feels normal when you don't have to see the real death.

I am not vegan, but I am optically conscious of what I eat, understanding whatever was alive had to be sacrificed to be consumed. I struggle with knowing that a life was taken for me to survive. That life in that package died so we could choose a meal to eat. And personally, I would not be able to kill the animal myself to survive, so when I buy any animal product, I'm cognizant that something had to be killed for my meal. Next time you walk into a supermarket, open your eyes and notice the scope of over-death that occurs in one supermarket alone. Walk through the frozen foods section and understand that every single meat package, at one time, had a beating heart.

So, I ask again, is another celebrity frozen meal dinner option really something we need? To me, it feels like a disingenuous, hypocritically greedy scam designed to obtain more wealth. If you go naked for PETA and animal rights, why on Earth are you killing more animals on a mass scale? Why are you okay with making people less healthy and more addicted to sugars and sodium instead of staying the line for the rights of animals? The hypocrisy is as rotten as the food.

These are the questions we should all be asking when we read our screens and watch our televisions. We lose ourselves in the story that these characters play. We believe they are aspirational, if not angelic, because they seem like they are just like you and me. We think they're on our team, and speaking the language of honesty properly. Meanwhile, they are profiting off our health, off our addictions and diseases as they hypocritically smile at their private chefs making them a five-star dinner you'll never be able to eat. "Don't do as I do—do as I say, and thank you all for making me wealthy."

We have the Food and Drug Administration approving food they know we should never consume. We have governmental agencies who are anti-marijuana but okay with, and possibly help distribute, addictive pharmaceuticals. It seems like the best drug dealers only need to wear lab coats to skate the system. The more chemicals we consume, the more we are in pain. The more processed food we throw into our bodies, the more profits they all receive. It feels like a hush-hush agreement to approve unhealthy food items on the front side in order to profit on the back side through the healthcare industry.

Control of our health begins with the food industry. I think these agencies stamp their approval on trash products like Skittles and Coke—things with little or no health benefit to us—just to get us hooked. Let's take sugar, for example. They addict children on sugar aggressively and early on to get them used to the feeling, so they'll continue to make poor food decisions until it's middle age and health issues begin. Sugar is far worse for our bodies than marijuana, and marijuana even has some medicinal benefits. But people go to prison for possessing too much weed while sugar, on the other hand, is not only approved but heavily marketed for consumption.

They allow catchy marketing ads of processed food products we should never allow into our bodies and allow drug companies to make ads for drugs we should never use. Have you ever actually listened to what some of those drug pills could do to your life? "This pill may cause sudden death. If you experience uncontrollable vomiting, seek medical attention." Again, the control being implemented all in the name of profits is insane.

We've been conditioned to accept that a small label on a package by a food and drug administration means it is safe for us to use. But make no mistake–it is just a cutthroat money grab, used to abuse our bodies for profit while weakening our health. They do not want what's best for you–they want what's inside of you to make money off you. And it is easy for them because control is ignored once you believe an agency's approval means you're in the hands of people looking out for you.

I want to believe control is a moral struggle for the people who possess wealth and power. I would think it has to be a moral struggle, even if these people are working with 50 percent empathy in their hearts. But control is hard to let go of, and these individuals and entities do not play by the rules, because they do not have to.

Imagine for a moment you are sitting on top of a beautiful mountain with a gorgeous view. How aggressively would you defend that view at all costs? Would you invite others up to the top to enjoy it with you? Or lie and manipulate to keep people away because you don't want to spoil the view? It's a challenging question, even though to those in power, it probably isn't challenging at all. They are already in control, and we are not their problem anymore because they are no longer a part of the controlled herd.

The moral thing to do will hardly ever be done. We're living in a world in which we must accept the controls being placed upon the individual and our society. We must recognize we live in a world where those in power will stop at nothing to further their control. The more these big data companies own us, the more they can abuse us. And the more those in power lie and manipulate us, the more they keep us divided and weak. We are failing ourselves without being told to do so. We must start seeing the hypocrisies staring at us. We must begin to be critical of what they are taking from us and selling to us if we ever have a shot at keeping our minds free. Our thoughts and our speech are the last lines of defense. And if we fail—if we do not wise up to the stories we're being sold—I fear the only view of Wyoming left will need to be purchased from a digital app.

dally london

theory of MATH

Life is subtracted
as they add up our lives.

If you are not good at math or merely dislike talking about math, do not worry—you are not alone. And before I lose your interest prior to even beginning this chapter, the following pages will not be asking you to solve equations, learn theorems, or look up definitions. Trust me, I would be a fraud to say I'm remotely versed in mathematics. Instead, I want you to think about math in a broader context.

I want you to see math in various abstract ways regarding how critical math is to our beginning and possibly our ending.

I'm not a mathematician or a physicist, so there is no need to research my credentials. I assume I'm closer to a commonality with you in terms of knowledge about mathematics than with Archimedes. I'm just an artistic poet philosopher walking down rabbit holes, thinking about the meaning of life, kicking up a little dust along the way. And you might be wondering then, how can a poet philosopher even talk about math without understanding it fully? I suppose the starting point, to begin with, is what in the hell is math?

On the surface, the answer is relatively simple. We all know what math looks like through our varied levels of education and study. Most, if not all of us, had eyes on at least a form of math beginning at a young age. But have you ever wondered, how did math come to be? Is math a thread line of language the early humans stumbled upon that will eventually lead us to the origins of creation? Removing all barriers from our minds of what we know and what we've been told about math, the answers start to come into focus.

Before we begin down this vast rabbit hole, I am going to prove real quickly how you, I, and Einstein have something in common mathematically. This will hopefully level set the table, so we're all on an equal footing of mental understanding. None of us—not me, you, not the most brilliant minds alive now or ever—know the answers to why we exist or how existence came to be. If, for example, you believe in the Big Bang Theory, then what created the "before" the Big Bang? And if something, or nothing, created the Big Bang, what created the something, or the nothing, that created the bang? Something had to make something, even if "the something" is actually nothing. Applying this logic to each of us, we all seem to be equally brilliant in our ignorance of the overarching life definition of our existence. Your guess is as good as mine or Einstein's.

I personally believe math is one of two things: the language of the universe or a cosmic disease infecting us. Even if you're the most enthusiastic Darwin supporter and the staunchest of evolutionary believers—when did the celestial light bulb fire on its light to bring about common languages, written glyphs, and spoken sounds? If we evolved into our species, when did the light of these things start to shine for humans?

Most folks know the adage, "What comes first, the chicken or the egg?" It's not really a game per se, but it is a never-ending loop of unsolvable question marks. You cannot have an egg without a chicken, but you cannot have a chicken without an egg. Using this old adage, think about the complexity of the English language. Did glyphs—letters, numbers, and symbols—create a sound, or did a sound make the glyph? To be able to say that a geometric glyph (a, b, c, 1, 2, 3, et cetera) even makes a sound is an absolutely fascinating concept. Think about the depth of a single letter. Where did the first letter originate?

And even more fascinating, putting several letters together forms a word with its own sound based on the relationship of each letter. And then otherworldly brilliance occurs when a collection of words creates a sentence with complex emotion and meaning and depth trying to explain a message of thought. If you take a step back and analyze this sentence, isn't it absolutely alien to think you just read a series of symbols combined in various ways, and you are able to comprehend what is written?

It seems at one point in time, we were far more in agreement with each other about desperately wanting to understand each other—what we actually meant and truthfully felt. It appears at some point in time, agreeableness to form a standard written and spoken dialect was in demand, enough so that humans either made symbols or drew symbols and gave them an agreed-upon sound to make communication possible.

Imagine having the same task today—to form an agreed-upon language. We're too individualistically emotional nowadays to develop a robust language in agreeable terms. I would argue the demand is low right now to even understand each other while being able to, given the suppression of speech occurring online these days. We live in a time where folks cannot even get their neighborhood block to agree on lawn care for their front yards, let alone form a complex language.

To say any glyph or symbol has any meaning to it, you would have to have some other driving force demanding its creation. Take LOL (laughing out loud), for example. LOL is now part of a ubiquitous vernacular we currently use in our modern-day communication. But those symbols, sounds, and meanings weren't always true. The LOL acronym is so apparent to us now and consequently adopted as part of society's dialogue—especially online—that it will never be removed as part of our dialect. It's now commonplace and accepted in many cultures. But there absolutely was a day before LOL ever existed. Someone or something had to be at the origin of its creation. And just like the LOL example, there had to be a day when "math" was born and a day before "math" was born. Could math be the unspoken universal language we've always known in our bones or the building block of all creation, the foundation of the universe's home?

Using the prior chicken or egg adage logic, what came first: spoken and written language or the language of math? Did language predate the unearthing of math? Or did math predate the unearthing of language? If humans created math to explain what math is, and we know unequivocally humans cannot be trusted to tell the truth, how do we know—for a fact—math is even true? Is math an invention of perceived realities? Think about it for a moment. We didn't find math symbols or theorems etched on cave walls solving life equations in prehistoric times. The symbols did not write themselves. Someone or something had to have made up math, either through accident, by human need, or by a visionary gift.

At some point in time, though, math did come

into life's focus. Math became understood and adopted as a universal language humans were instructed to learn. And if humans created math to explain certain worldly things, then are we merely expanding on a made-up language construct other humans created? Is it possible math is the biggest lie we've ever been told?

There seem to be gaps in the "truths" math tells. Even today, there are disagreeing anomalies between the theory of general relativity and the predictions of quantum mechanics. And a common practice amongst scientists, physicists, and mathematicians is to recognize then set aside those anomalies—observe it, and continue on.

It's evident to me that math is much more than a discovery by humans designed for calculation. Instead, I believe math is a foreign language created by and understood by the universe. It's an alien, omnipotent dialect greater than any species, planet, or galaxy. And no, I do not mean the antennas-on-the-head type of aliens when I say alien—but rather math is a foreign language that builds the skin of the universe and is spoken and understood throughout the cosmos.

Planet to planet, galaxy to galaxy, math seems to predate every language we know. Even if humans on Earth didn't know what math was upon becoming conscious beings, I believe it stitched together the world. We walk through math, we drink it, and we breathe it. We are even tattooed internally with a numerical code of math–a DNA sequence hidden inside our blood, identifying how unique we are. Primarily, we are all made of math.

What I cannot quite grasp, however, is how primitive humans would have understood this complexity at all. Math means nothing without understanding the definitions of a communication language first. This is my own mental black hole of logic I'm trying to sort out. Take adding, for example. Adding didn't mean "to add" until someone formed a common written and communicable language stating adding meant to add. How does "adding" mean anything before the term "adding" itself is defined? How did someone know how to count before determining what counting meant?

One is both a number and a word. It is a symbol with a human interpretation of its meaning. The little geometric glyph we all see and know as "1" holds otherworldly meaning in its mathematical design. But was "1" a number first that meant a word, or a word first that meant a number? What did one mean before one existed, and what created the symbol to give it meaning? This is a constant, problematic logic loop I cannot remedy.

To most of us, math is an established given. The language of math is so universal and innate to us now we assume it to be an actual part of our lives without giving it much thought. We adopted math since before we have the memories of its introduction to us in pre-school or kindergarten. But if you walk your mind back far in time, you will reach a point on the continuum where math did not exist. At this specific point on the continuum, math was not an established truth. It was the horizon of a new frontier for human beings–a black hole yet to be flown into. It was locked away in the elements of the primitive day's existence–to be discovered by humans by evolution or given to them somehow. And "given to" means either shown by an array of life problems the humans needed to solve or by a foreign entity or a God helping to assist them to solve its riddle.

Math had to be a dormant language, hidden in plain sight, at some point in time. Quite possibly, humans didn't even know what math meant until they started to give it sound and value. Numbers were not numbers until they were drawn. Numbers didn't have a noise associated with them until they became vocalized through human sound. Maybe every time a human made a noise or a grunt for a patterned action, the primitive humans tried to understand and quantify it by giving it a shape. Perhaps they used straight-line soot markings on the cave walls to define the number "1." Maybe at first, it was just an artistic representation of a single human. "1" looked like a human standing upright, and they used multiple 1's to verify the number of humans in their tribe. You and I would be "1, 1." Or maybe they used these markings to signify instances of whatever animal or edible harvest they were tracking or collecting. Perhaps it was humans looking at gathered firewood and needing to calculate quantity to see if they had enough to survive. Or maybe it was the food rations or the water supply, and the application was designed to use a single mark to keep track of everything.

Now that we've walked back to the possible origins of remedial counting, race your mind forward on life's continuum a bit to when math became the separation between the survived and the deceased. Math had to eventually become an agreement amongst the individuals living within the tribe. Those humans who learned to count and learned to flex the math muscle furthered the survival of themselves and the tribe. Knowing quantities and needs became critical to the survival of the individual and the tribal community. Being mathematically wrong meant the difference between life and death.

I can visualize the use case of needing math to survive each day while humans faced the harshest conditions in a barren world void of communication. If humans at the time knew the food or water supply was too low to keep themselves alive, the need had to require action on behalf of the tribe. Tracking the inventory of supply could have been the rationale for the need for a common language while helping math take shape.

If we did not default to the knowledge of math, then math must have circled around us, making itself known. It currently swirls around us in everyday life. Math is the water we drink, the air we breathe, the fire we burn. It is the music we hear, the graphics we see, the love we feel. Math is a base form sequence of true or false Boolean choice types–on/off switches of 1's and 0's–that define almost everything we do. Are you alive "1" or dead "0"? Are you female "1" or male "0"? Are you happy "1" or sad "0"? Are you starving "1" or nourished "0"? Is it the night

"1" or day "0?" This base form of "binary" math, then, seems to be the basis for connecting all of us together. If this logic is true, then we've been given math since the beginning of time, even before we were cognitively aware of it. Math, then, could be the DNA flowing through the universe's blood, keeping it alive.

I believe this unspoken binary sequence of 1's and 0's to be the genesis of all existence. Imagine the humans at the beginning of evolutionary time–confused, cold, and alone–in the vastness of uninhabited Earth. Imagine how lonely it must have been unable to communicate thoughts and feelings, unable to distinguish objects as friend or foe, and having trial and error as the only way to know if something would kill you. I often wonder, since basic binary–the 1/0 on/off construct—has been with us since the beginning of time, is math the actual sound of the universe's heartbeat? On (1) and off (0). Find the rhythm of your heartbeat and apply this binary to the sound–on and off, on and off. Does math hold the key to who we are?

In the day-one human scenario, math, albeit unknown to the earliest humans, would be the only thing they could have relied upon. The first humans would be forced into a binary equation of surviving (1) or dying (0), afraid (1) or unafraid (0). It is not a mistake math was shown to them before they understood it. They needed basic logic to negotiate decisions. And because of this binary on/off construct every human had to navigate, math can only be described as the foundation of creation and the baseline language of the universe. If the universe is designed in math, and our planet is made of math, then humans must be, too. And this math in our lives continually connects members of our species to each other, growing from a primitive binary connection to modern-day artificial-intelligence infection.

Throughout time, we've considered math to be the fun (or fun for some), benign language. It's a powerful language. Its explanations have, without a doubt, led to the betterment of our global community. We've become conditioned to use it to for common-day utilities such as balancing bank accounts, adding up the costs of items and calculating distances between cities. Most of us have also cursed it for making us do assessment tests of its theories during our schooling. But is math a bit more wicked than it seems? Is math more of a malignant enemy than a benign friend? Is it more like a diseased, alien language calculating the days until we end our own species? Maybe what once was guiding us into the light of life is now guiding us into the abyss of darkness. Is math evolving out of our control, or is it an infection—infecting us—that we've helped grow?

In the current era, algorithms and computer systems rely almost absolutely on a binary coding system of 1's and 0's. Sound familiar? The phone you hold is virtually 100 percent made of math. The operating system is, without a doubt, made of math. The pictures you take on your phone? Visual math. When you press the "keyboard" on your phone that types letters or numbers? Graphical math. The social media feeds you see on your phone? Content math. The number of likes or followers you have? Algorithmic math.

Our screens are using calculations of math to display representations of what we're familiar with. The smallest interaction on our devices takes a galaxy of mathematical logic to execute. The keyboard on your phone, for example, isn't a keyboard at all, but it definitely resembles one. In actuality, the keyboard is just math. The screen on the phone you hold in your hand, maybe even right now reading this if you have the eBook, is a visual representation of brilliant math calculations using the same 1's and 0's primitive humans used, just on a much, much grander scale. It's funny to think about, but if you fast-forward 10,000 years from now, there could be selfies of math on our phones' "cave walls" that future generations will not understand.

Maybe on the continuum of existence, we are only at the beginning of what the universe wants itself to become. And maybe math is helping it come to life—era by era—right before our eyes. Math led us to today through mutations in our minds. And math will lead us into the future, but will it always be kind? Math simply needs to find a "host" to infect to grow itself. The "host species" would only need to be intelligent enough to understand the story math desires to tell.

Most humans cannot understand the depth of math very well or understand its needs. I know I checked out after calculus class in school. But the geniuses? They float their minds in the sky and see math clear as day. They pour math into their morning coffee and stir it in. But maybe the geniuses of each era were only hand-picked, human hosts to help get math to the point of today, where it is unlocking artificial intelligence. Maybe this math "disease" used these geniuses to build our species' coffin since robots will be far more durable, unemotional, and advanced. And because math can evolve and grow inside of robot "host species" at a much higher volume and speed, the need for humans will one day cease to exist. Sound far-fetched? Not to me.

Look at the brilliant minds as dots on a linear map throughout existence. It's easy to see these dots of genius innovation mapping the path to the current modern-day artificial intelligence. Many intellectuals were inspired by an obsession to understand the universe. Each of them was solving the blind spots of the other, collectively finding the answers to the last one's unsolvable problems. Each was a stone rung on the giant artificial-intelligence ladder. Each too, it seems, personally believed their brilliance was intended to help further humanity, which in most cases, is absolutely right. But looking back retrospectively, were these geniuses mere pawns in the game of artificial intelligence?

Genius thinking may have helped build the car we're collectively about to drive off the cliff. And it seems—unfortunately—most modern-day geniuses are interested in profitability and greed, not furthering our species. So who is looking out for us now? It begs the question when a dollar sign is next to a moral decision, do you genuinely believe care for human existence is the driving factor?

If a self-driving algorithm in a truck causes millions to lose their jobs but increases the company's profits, will they build them anyway? Sadly if one company doesn't build the self-driving vehicle (they already have made them), another company will. It only takes a dip in moral philosophy by one company to ignore the impact "innovation" will have on fellow humans. The innovation, once considered the brilliance of the curious minds helping lives, is now leading to the eradication and consumption of the human mind. Math's evolution, you see, could be the geniuses blind spot disease.

We seem to be at a point in time where we are willingly okay with robots usurping humans on the dominance hierarchy. You might even be silently telling me to shut up in your mind. "Who cares if that happens?" some may think, "if a phone listens to me or if math reads data points on my face and stores it on my digital record, why does it matter?"

And maybe those who think that way are correct. But in my opinion, we are closing in on the apex of human potential, mathematically speaking. We cannot walk outside and fly like a bird, we cannot live underwater, and our thumbs hold us back from communicating faster. Our ceiling has been met in almost all our physical and mental capabilities. Now, we seem destined to build artificial intelligence that can calculate at higher levels while learning and evolving itself at blinding speeds, faster than any human or humans ever could.

Robotic artificial intelligence will soon drive our cars, will think for us, will type for us, and will speak for us. AI will soon be a necessity to survive, not merely just an accent to our lives. The survival of the fittest could become the survival of the most subserviently connected. You might, one day, have to insert an artificial chip into your body to avoid being deemed a rebel to the AI cause, or an outcast to society. You might have to kneel to the AI gods and embrace its control to prevent personal genocide.

You'll have to trust the mathematical species by a societal mandate because you are now the luxury it will no longer need to have. And once that takes place, and the robotic AI is in power, what good will humans be to the world, other than destroying resources? If the AI is continually having to help us to survive, when will the AI become tired of being our "slaves"?

Modern-day geniuses are working toward giving AI an autonomous, self-improving conscience, or what some classify as "the singularity." They want the AI to process the world as humans do, and be able to use critical thinking to make decisions as it evolves itself without human interaction. They are focused on using math to give AI everything a human has–but much more. And the scary part is, they aren't as far away from achieving it as you think. I wonder, in the depths of their minds, are the technology companies of the world and the geniuses of today aware they are playing god with life's existence?

Humanity does not stand a chance in the future.

If you think about it, we are already cyborgs. Your phone is as much a part of you as you are. And no one can convince me that in 200 years, humans will still be liberated free (if we even exist.) Math's tentacles are already becoming sequenced around our minds through the misinformation of AI. It is no longer a sleeping, benign language that once helped us learn the world. It is very much awake, salivating at building the next world.

As we become further distracted with selfies, emojis, and robotic assistants, we ignore the fact our minds are under attack. We're in the infancy of this technology era, and there is no going back. It is difficult to grasp math's wrath of future job elimination, the removal of real human interactions, and the severity of artificial intelligence's control on our lives. One day, in the not-so-distant future, I fear the need for humans altogether will be gone. AI built with math is beginning to understand that the more we're advancing its own creation, the more infected we become by it. And the more infected we become, the less dependency math has for us. We will keep evolving past ourselves until we develop something more advanced than us that lacks the need and care for us. This is an absolute certainty. Humans will be an outdated equation, and robots will be the next generational species to be used for its advancement.

The more we give away our private lives, the more math algorithmically grows. The more we consume it, the more it grows. The more we supply it, the more it grows. This future view of the world is a blindness only the wisest are able to visualize. These math algorithms are not tactile and do not have a shape, yet. You cannot pick them up and hold them with your hands. But soon, math will be free of our control, and AI will be able to further itself autonomously. Math may have been the binary result of our beginning, but most certainly seems to be the solution of our end.

We only see 5 percent of the universe, but math sees 100 percent. Earth could very well be the collective coffin we're all burying ourselves in through the development of artificial intelligence. But if Earth speaks in the language of math, maybe it will be an ally for us in this future AI war. Perhaps as AI grows, Earth is just a stepping stone along the way in the continuum of what the universe is destined to become. Or maybe math is really a benign friend, rotating with us through infinity, to save us from extinction. Math could be the riddle of life or the ruination of existence–the "anything" and the "everything"–whispering the language of the god of gods we need to listen intently to hear. For 66 million years we evolved on this planet but grew at a cosmically slow marathon pace. And in just the last 200 years, we sprinted into an evolutionary advancement we may never recover from.

Maybe there isn't a beginning to our own equation. Perhaps it's more of a loop–a loop of life that doesn't end. And this could be why we do not see cave drawings of addition, or subtraction, or theorems and equations. This could be why we lack any real understanding of who we are and why we are. We build ourselves up using math in the game of life, and we destroy ourselves every time. If life is just a game played by math to find the meaning of life and command the universal language, then maybe we are close to the end of time this time. Perhaps our game is at the last level, and the advancement of a few more generations will lead us to the game being over. If artificial intelligence is the predetermined result of math's growth and we just never learn to stop it, then maybe we're evolving in a loop exactly how we should–cycles and lifetimes of trial and error.

I believe the game the gods want us to play is loving each other and the universe. The end of the game is showing the gods we've forgotten how we got here, when the addition of innovation starts equaling subtraction of life.

dally london

theory of

SADNESS

Why be an offline human
when you can be an online god?

The end of the analog society is approaching, and there isn't much we can do to slow it down. Most of us these days are too dialed into the online content-driven world, and our children's children, unfortunately, will not have a choice to unplug from it. Social media is already a cancerous disease infecting our minds and changing our lives, but it is just the beginning of the digital revolution yet to come.

This online mesmerization of being liked and loved is augmenting what it feels like to actually be liked and loved. Love is now mostly being controlled transactionally in social media applications and sits atop an online world filled with illusions of success and popularity.

I recently ran a test on Instagram. I pressed the blue "Promote" button on several of the poems on my feed to see what effects such a transaction would cause. Amazingly, I grew almost 9,000 followers in a few weeks–from 40,000 to 49,000–after paying money to Facebook (Facebook owns Instagram, so technically, I paid Facebook.) And each promoted post nearly quadrupled in the number of likes and views I received. Some may say this shows the effectiveness of social promotion, and that is fair. But when did the monetization and controlling of free speech become an accepted narrative we agreed upon?

"Success" is being viewed nowadays in how many likes someone's posts receive. We've been trained, through addiction, to feel good when our content is followed and liked. But if you're only being seen if you pay money to Instagram/ Facebook, then the monetarily wealthiest voices will rise, and the rest will drown. The ramifications of this control on our self-worth seem very, very grim. It's no surprise suicides are on an astronomical rise.

We are not searching for or finding truth online. We are desperately trying to feed the addiction of our disease, scrolling through social feeds for self-esteem boosts and acceptance, through the pulses of faceless individuals we don't know and probably will never meet. We are evolving digital worlds into fairytale truths, even if we know this online fantasy is seldom, if ever, replicated in the real world. What seems popular online is probably paid for in some way, and whose voice gets heard, a matter of how willing the person is to open their pocketbook.

As we navigate through these social media feeds, we absorb, believe, and engage emotionally without pause for thought. The factual truths of information are being controlled and sold, and our emotions are under attack. We will not understand the impacts of these social media platforms on our society for years to come, and possibly will never fully know, since the scientific data is being controlled by private algorithms.

We are rapidly being herded by algorithms into digital tribes rot with radical thinking, dying individualism, and divisive uncertainty. The offline world doesn't feel or seem this way to me. The offline world looks less divided and more accepting of each other, and more individualistically free. Individuals I see in the coffee shop, going to the movies, or dining, seem more alike than different. But in the online world, our individual identities ache for tribal relevancy. We seem compelled to post information desirable enough to feed the popular tribe's energy, and to come across as "awake" or "woke" while simultaneously feeding our "persona's" ego. When we open the online world, we are mostly presented with the controlled opinions, rich idealism, and ideological philosophy that paint a perception of right and wrong, good and evil. Who is popular enough to receive attention and reactions is filtered through the algorithm's mind (and bank account.) And because of this, we too are starting to mold ourselves into reflections of "popular" speech.

Because we are the arbiters of our online identity that lives on the screen, we often act as chameleons, shaping ourselves into the "correct perception" when beneficial. We can choose to show the entire essence of who we actually are and what we believe by posting every single genuine action and thought we have, or we can build an online persona and craft the narrative to the information we want the world to believe. The difference between the real person and the created persona is often worlds apart, but how can you ever really know?

With social media, it is a game we all play even if we are not aware we are playing it. We cannot see behind the phone, tablet, or laptop posting news, pictures, and stories. We cannot fact check every narrative preached from the pulpit of a person's device. We are left with defaulting to a "believe or not believe" negotiation based on unclear facts and emotional assumptions, frequently forming opinions based on what the tribe we most ascribe to thinks.

It seems to me our addiction to the utopia perpetuated through online personas and stories is changing the truth of society. The baseline lie of "facts" being told online is weaved so systematically through our minds, we are now starting to prefer its drama to our real life's normalcy. The stories told online feel cinematic, almost movie-like, with gotcha moments, arch enemies, death, and destruction. This drunken fairytale of social media information is so appealing, some will compromise their own life, their own art, their own personal relationships just to partake in the madness.

Quiz yourself the next time you are in public. Gaze around the crowds of people in restaurants, coffee shops, airports and stores, and count the faces focused downward, staring into the digital abyss of their phones. If we continue down this path, we may evolve our species one day to be born with chins touching our chest. It is socially assumed if not accepted nowadays, that for us to survive in the modern world, we must be connected at all times. The online world, you see, now controls the offline world, and the offline world is always "alive" even when we sleep.

In all fairness, there does seem to be a silent minority vocalizing disdain for what is happening on social media. Maybe you have even said it before to yourself, "I am done with social media," or "I think I'm going to quit social media," though our actions always speak louder than our words. Have you unplugged from social media yet? I would assume not since even thinking about it probably makes your heart skip a beat, feeling as if you will miss something important, and be forgotten by society. The digital drug inside your devices might be so addictive, you may have even caught yourself looking at your texts or checking your social media feeds before finishing this chapter. The digital cry for our eyes and our minds is loud, is it not?

Our lives now orbit two conflicting worlds: the offline layer, or stratum, of who we are and how we behave in the physical world, and the online stratum, one that projects who we are and how we act in the digital world. In the digital stratum, the speech is controlled and narratives manipulated to a higher degree than in the offline world, inherently putting them in conflict with each other. This is not to say we cannot do the same controlling and manipulating in our offline world. We create fairytales and manipulate people and situations all the time. It is, however, far easier to hide behind lies and puppeteer individuals and conversations in an online world that exists solely inside of a fixed-screen device lacking depth.

Our eyes will struggle to focus on the truth when our vision is constantly being blurred. To highlight this example, when someone posts something to a social media feed, how believable do you think the pictures and captions are when it is being consumed at sound bite speed? Glimpses of information are not the entire truth being told, but we build these outlandish stories from them. We connect dots to complete an assumption. We tease out worlds in our minds from a picture and caption stuck in time, posted by people we (mostly) do not know, filled with emotional facts in a context we'll never fully comprehend. This leads us to change the chemistry of truth, and feel more attached to and educated about a person or subject matter, even though we are more than likely becoming factually less knowledgeable. We want to believe what we see and read, and desperately want the person behind each post to be genuine and honest. We believe their persona to be a projection of realism, so we default to absorbing almost all the information without challenge. But just because a tiny crack in the window of their digital home allowed us to peek our eyes in, does not mean we know what is going on inside the house.

Do you ever stop and think about what or who

is behind the social media posts you like? Let your mind take a stroll for a second, and try to walk behind the phone of someone posting. See their eyes glowing from their phone's light, and their smirk widening as the glee flows while they type away. Humanize their posts and try to grasp the "why" behind the pressing of the "Share" button. If you can do this exercise, the context of each post changes. Knowing that somewhere on the planet, that post is just a person, just like you, holding their device, might make it easier to normalize their larger-than-life personas. Would they say this same thing in public, or say it to someone's face? Would you accept them speaking this way?

Everything and everyone has an agenda even if the agenda is relatively benign. The agenda could be telling the truth or showing something interesting to engage with people in a reasonable way. There are plenty of genuinely "good" people in this world. But for the most part, the agenda is to change the facts and perpetuate a lie or to cause people to react. But again, if you can visualize there is a person behind each post, you can start to read between the lines to see the actual truth. There is a person holding a digital weapon in their palm, and we only see the result of each bullet they fire. "Leave out this fact" but "include this fact," or use divisive language to skew meaning, even though they know it is egregiously unfair but "gets more attention." One of my favorites is those who show themselves naked in a post but claim "only getting attention for my body" makes them angry.

Facts are being blurred online to get more attention and gain notoriety. Personas are manipulated to make "real people" a tad bit "cooler" than their actual selves. Our society has normalized content consumption to the point that we're now conditioned to trust the sound bites we scroll through. It begs the question, who can we trust anymore? There is almost zero chance we can keep up with the context of information when blurring facts is the new true vision.

Let's use a hypothetical example both of us can visualize. Think of a couple right now in your mind. Try to think of a couple who is in a relationship. You may even be in one yourself right now. Many couples post photos online of their lives, the events they attend, the happiness of their days, and their accomplishments together. But for this example, try to think of an overly happy couple and see them in your mind to work through the following few sentences.

This happy couple currently at the forefront of your mind post pictures often about their perfect life. They travel to pristine beaches, attend seemingly popular social events, and always look as if they own the world in all their social media posts. For argument's sake, let's say all of their posted content happens to be accurate, and they are genuinely happy. On the scroll of your social feed, you are still only seeing the outcome of their happiness—nothing more. The joy in their pictures feels tangible to you because everything they post on social media tells you that story. And maybe personally, when you see these pictures, sadness washes over you because your life isn't as perfect as theirs. Or, envy begins to blossom inside your mind because you want the experiences they project for yourself. Or, maybe hope fills your heart because they are proving true happiness does exist, making you more optimistic about life. Whatever feeling you have, just seeing their social posts affects your body's chemistry.

What if this happy online couple you're visualizing in your mind right now isn't happy at all? Perhaps the happiness projected by this couple in these social media posts is just an illusion—an agreed-upon lie to publicly convey a life better than the life they actually live. Any chance that they get to manipulate the truth of who they are, they capitalize on with ferocity, so the online world believes the story they want to sell. But privately, in the offline world, they're brutally miserable. They dare not post the "before the beach" fight they had at the hotel, or the "after dinner" fight they had at the bar because those moments do not tell the story they want you to believe. They want you to think they are a perfect couple, with a perfect life, and staging pictures will feed everyone the fairytale.

The moments captured in any instance and shared on social media are split-second fragments plucked from time. Everyone is a digital actor online, and we publish "life" onto a digital stage for the world to see. Almost all social media posts are manufactured to feed society some version of a lie. The online paradises we visit—so to speak—become illusions of pristine waters under cloudless skies, while in actuality, waves rage in stormed-up oceans. And because we lack the context of content, mentally, we will always see the seas as perfectly blue even if the skies are violent, since we only absorb life online in glimpses.

Hiding in plain sight online is rather easily accomplished when you are in control of all the facts and truths you wish to show. Without guidance and accountability existing in the digital stratum, we'll never be able to find the truth. We are a social media "like" away from becoming absorbed into the vanity of anyone's illusion, the truthful lie they want you to believe, not who they actually are in the physical world.

For example, maybe in a social media post, someone desires to be a bit more in shape, and the next post a bit more successful, a bit stronger, a bit wealthier, or a bit more popular. In an online world where you are the ruler of your own domain, you set all the rules. You create and manipulate all the facts. It is the person behind the device posting content who controls the outcomes we see and read. So all these hard-working, physical items in the offline stratum someone must work years to achieve are now a "roll-over-in-bed" moment away from digital attainment. If someone desires to be more popular? Hey, make up a success or an accomplishment. You will receive unearned acceptance because everyone will assume it truly happened. If someone needs sympathy? Craft a fake tragedy or situation in your life. I promise you, you will find compassion and well-wishes to your fakery on social media.

An example occurred on social media last year when a person decided to show the aftermath of cutting themselves in their Instagram story. The "story" was shown as a cry for help, with some alarming content posted alluding to the ending of this person's life, showing slashes of red marks across the arm, while having a rather large glass of wine. If you were to believe this "story," which most did, then perhaps you would have been shocked and terrified, and trying to help this person. But your worries would have been for naught. The only notable concern of this entire event was the fact the actual "self-harm" didn't happen. The real cry for help seemed to echo less from a person and more from a bank account. The "self-harm" seemed to be attached to the marketing promotion of a business project with an upcoming product release that week.

So it seems, if you want to come across as edgy, in pain, and troubled even if you're not, create a story and watch the sympathetic comments materialize. You might be thinking, clearly, everyone noticed this and called out this possible marketing stunt, but not many did. The person did not take a character hit at all because no one knew what to believe. How could anyone know the truth of anything besides what they were being shown? And you cannot call someone a liar without the facts. Many of the comments posted addressed mental health issues and implored the person to seek help. Hardly anyone cared about the marketing aspect of the gimmick and instead offered genuine support to someone in need, even though this person was apparently being deceptive in their cries for help.

I cannot get inside the mind of a person who would think to do a stunt like that, but I sincerely hope this person is seeking help, obviously for reasons other than the "fake" cutting. Is it criminal to use tactics like self-harm to increase product sales? I don't know. Morally bankrupt, for sure. But this somewhat proves to me, however, that without all the facts, any story can be weaved into our minds as factually accurate. We are a chameleon species with diabolical capabilities, and trusting anyone's online persona by default is a practice we should all rethink.

In an online world that exists without constraints, the survival of the species is not necessarily based on who is the fittest. Survival morphs into who can control their outcomes the best and who can manipulate society the best. These digital castles individuals build and lord over online will never be accountable to anyone, because they are their own judges and juries, holding court over their entire world without punishment.

On the surface, this power structure of people being their own ruler resembles real freedom, with both sides of the coin having their face on it. But this absolute freedom is an illusion of fool's gold. For example, if I fake everything I do online to project and embolden a false persona, am I simply a good manipulator? Will the successes only be as good as the stories I tell? Are people in love with the idea of me and not the real me?

I wonder, if every social media account had to come with a five-minute interview of their actual self, how many would fight to hide from it.

The online version of yourself comes with significant responsibilities. If we are left to our own devices, figuratively and literally, do we default to being good or being bad? Some of us do default to being as honest as we can be and try not to partake in gimmicks or tricks. But the gap between honesty and manipulation is a small, confusing margin, especially when we cannot separate fiction from nonfiction.

For most, the fool's gold reward of projecting the online persona fairytale far supersedes the humility of being honest and truthful. The intoxication and popularity received from manipulating the truth are far too high to ever give up, even if it is exhausting. The life they are capable of building and managing in the online world is much better than the life they actually have, so being honest isn't even a consideration. With that stored inside your mind, you have to consider the persona online is not a reflection of the person offline. Remedial logic states that a chameleon will by default manipulate while living in a world unchecked. If you can be an online god, why be an offline human?

Most of us start our days with a little lie believing the "you" reflected in the mirror is a correct representation. The mirror we look into daily, however, actually demonstrates the opposite of the truth, presenting back to us the reverse view of our own self. We are surrounded by lies and stories of half-truths all the time. It is our default way of seeing. Not only that, but we further these lies by embellishing stories and adding romance words to make life more interesting. And in the online world, where visual cues are hidden and intuition is muted, it's hard to negotiate between the truth and the lie.

As intoxicating as it might be to build up the online people you've never met into modern-day kings and queens, there is a good to excellent chance the person who you follow on social media would not be someone you would follow offline. The online Superman oftentimes is not even Clark Kent in real life. They are probably incapable of saving you from a runaway buggy at the grocery store, let alone taking on the world. Mathematically speaking, online perception will rarely match the offline reality. The godlike perception will always be a fallacy of the online world. And if we are telling the truth, for 95 percent of us, life is not always as exciting as social media claims it to be.

It is now far too easy to augment a digital reality to fit lying narratives, and yet we continue to believe what we see. Truth, it seems, has been stripped of all factual periods and been replaced by romanticized question marks. We are now the reactors to brief video clips, fixed-time imagery, and short-form words posted to social media to show us what "life" currently resembles. We are reacting to snapshots of stalled time, weaving many years of stories about what we believe we just saw into a version of a false truth.

Are you aware there are "social media services" you can pay that will photoshop you into any location on the planet, to make your life seem more exciting than it is? Are you aware influencers, folks who apparently are "influential" and get paid to influence others, are actually living lives controlled by companies to market products to you? There is even a "pod" system some people use on social media, where they get into social "groups" and "manipulate" excitement about something posted to make their posts seem more relevant and popular. These subgroups of community members manipulate the system by having the group members like, comment, or share what they post. Every group member must like and comment on other members' posts, quality be damned, to fake importance and popularity. Instead of organic and real demand for their content, they push a manufactured demand. To the untrained eye, all this behavior seems legitimate.

I was invited into one of these social media "pod" groups in the poetry community. Initially, I turned the request down because I didn't know what it meant to be in a "pod." I've always been a lone wolf of sorts, introverted even in the offline world, so being "social" didn't gel well with my comfort zone. But after being sold on the story that the "pod" is meant to be a place where artists could critique each other's work, I decided to give it a shot and at least check it out.

I spent about a week inside the "pod," mostly observing. I engaged so little, the creator of the pod sent me a direct message telling me the rules of the pod system. The owner said the pod system isn't for everyone, but if you're going to be a part of it, you need to like and comment on everyone's "submission" when they post to the group. Obviously, I do not view appreciation of art this way, so I knew I wouldn't stay in the pod I'd been invited to for very long. But I did wait a few more days in order to see how they functioned.

The pod wasn't about artists critiquing words or a community of support for the art. The pod was simply a group of people committed to the goal of "you help me I help you," without care of quality or message. If you were in the group, then you were embraced. I watched as a group member would post into the pod to let people know they just posted, then immediately see each group member's name pop up in their post's comment section. "Brilliant, my queen." "You're amazing." "Couldn't have said it better." All disingenuous responses. All faux likes. And many of the pod members were in multiple pods, so you can imagine how much false "love" and appreciation is being spread around the art world.

The number of followers by a name on social media or the number of likes on a post may not be the truth of the story at all. The number beside the name could be an amalgamation of cheating to sidestep real success by utilizing false acceptance—all in the name of online fame. There are published authors out there right now on bookshelves who have bought and paid their way into stores. Many of the social media accounts manipulated their way to online royalty. I often wonder how they rest at night atop a bed of lies.

So, how can we ever know if the number beside the name is legitimately earned or not? Truth is, we no longer can. And I have scores of messages in my inbox on Instagram from companies and public accounts saying for a fee, they can grow followers and likes on any account. Money, it seems, can purchase the popularity drug.

We are living in a sad world these days, and living honestly is the only humane way to march our society forward, especially in the social media era. No, we cannot actually capture our analog life online into still images, pithy captions and small snippets of videos, but we can tell the most honest example of it. If you think about the concept of life, it is actually quite preposterous to assume reality could be cataloged in a sound bite way using a digital platform. Online truths are and always will be the idea of life, not the actuality of it.

If you go beyond the vanity of someone's social media post, what we're really seeing is the strategic planning of stories being told. There is a strong possibility that behind the device posting to a social media feed lives a strategic human being. The "successful" ones with many followers following their accounts, probably paid to grow to the number you see. And in this very controlled, strategic life are lies crafted to build a fairytale narrative in the most attractive way possible.

What escapes me in all this, however, is how common it is amongst people to try to perpetuate the idea of themselves instead of being honest about who they are. We toss common sense out the window just to keep this false online reality driving. Anyone at any moment is capable of staging a lie while promoting it as the truth. People are staging events that never happened, traumas that never occurred, breakups that never existed, all to gain sympathy and become more popular online. To me, it looks like we've gone mad with an addiction to social media.

The hierarchy of "power" and "importance" also being projected online is mostly inaccurate. Social media platforms have become a designer drug fixating on follower counts, and post likes to inject an illusion of online status. How many followers you have and how many likes you receive supposedly equates to how important you are. And it all depends on how desperate one is to see how far they will go to live their own lie.

To highlight what I mean, I'll use a hypothetical writer, since it's the world I know best. Also, for this example, and to keep the blade of the conversation sharpened to a fine point, I'll define "success" numerically both in terms of followers and likes on a post.

Imagine this hypothetical writer is a teller of pain, of hope, of love, and is a decent wordsmith. This writer is an undeniable "talent" (and I placed quotes around that on purpose, which I'll circle back to in a minute.) Now this person, this writer, seems quite educated, sociable, and put together. This writer is even revered within the writing community, accepted as a significant player by the popular crowd. In the online world, the writer seems as close to perfection as you can achieve—a strong voice, a stronger following, averages in the thousands of likes per post and has a few books for sale. But the rock-star persona being projected online by both the writer and the writing community is an entirely false one.

Let's say this hypothetical writer is middle-aged, lives at home in the basement, and is unemployed by choice. Hidden from the world, the writer's true identity isn't complementary to the persona, but instead, completely opposite of the projection. And behind the online facade of portraying this nice, successful artist, is a writer who espouses darkness. They speak ill about others, use manipulative tactics to deceive unassuming "fans" into sending personal photos, and find humor in the fact they're all being fooled. The writer is quite a contradiction to their online persona, but no one will ever know the truth since the writer is viewed as a "success."

Nonetheless, when this hypothetical writer

opens the online castle door, the offline jester becomes a very believable online king or queen. The projected persona puts on an online crown and becomes the exact opposite of the reality of life. You may say, well, this writer found their outlet to freedom—the freedom of who they believe they should be in an unaccepting offline world. And I would say, that is fair logic, albeit flawed. Because eventually, the crown of the online king or queen must come off when intersecting with the offline world. And to further this point, this hypothetical person may not be seeking an outlet of expression at all—but simply loves playing the populace for a fool in a kingdom of their own control. Talent, it would seem, has taken on an entirely new shape.

In the online kingdom, lying, bullying, manipulation, control, and the tearing down of individuals are all acceptable strategies. The online lie quickly becomes a truth, once in "power." The virtual life becomes real life to certain individuals once their follower counts grow, and the offline world isn't reality anymore. Meeting people in the offline world comes with a wink and a smirk. "If they only knew who I really am, they wouldn't believe it." It is as close to psychotic as we can get, but absolutely a real thought these individuals possess. And without any checks and balances of their validity on social media, the hurricane of lies will only grow stronger over time.

This type of behavior is more common than you think. These hypotheticals are far closer to the online reality than you could ever imagine. Many people in the online world know exactly how to abuse and control other people by selling them precisely what the reader wants to hear. And I would assume if most saw the actual reality of the truth living behind the screen of the device, they would be horrified they ever considered following them.

There needs to be a debate about the quality of content being published and consumed online. All speech has to be free from control, but the information we publish should be more authentic than ever before, given how we now absorb information in sound bites. The fact we neglect to pay attention nowadays means the onus is on the individual posting to social media to be as authentic as he or she can to normalize the truth. Our duty as bastions of history and ambassadors of our own species is to be even more honest in this social media era. We no longer have the luxury of a deep-diving society willing to understand information outside of a bite-sized, quick-glance context.

Unfortunately, we are evolving away from a culture with the desire to back up words with facts. Instead, we are interested in tearing each other down, selling popular lies, and creating the most popular persona possible. We've been introduced to the drug of constant consumption of pictures, and stories, and videos that make us feel smarter. Our eyes and minds are now trained to sidestep the effort of real learning, and the attainment of actual knowledge. We're conditioned to read the synopsis of the Cliff's Notes of life and beat the drum of our chest as if we are more knowledgeable than ever.

Why does this all matter? Well, I believe the digital stratum is leading us to civil unrest, suppression of speech, manipulation of truth, and, ultimately, division of species. One day soon, we won't be able to trust each other as we once may have, and we may be unable to separate truth from lie so easily. And when lies equal truths, it will be easier for the powerful to manipulate the unassuming, place controls on speech to affect what we hear and speak, and shape our society by telling us the reality we need to believe, instead of allowing us to think freely. And we should all want to lift up the truth to lift up our lives instead of dividing our culture by believing in "popular" lies.

theory of

CONCRETE

Wakes left in the ocean of life
wave forever.

We are constantly evolving, learning, and morphing our molds into new versions of ourselves as we absorb new information. There is a version of "you" before this book, and there will be a version of "you" after this book. There is even a version of "you" before this specific sentence began. A second ago, this sentence was new to you but now lives in the past. Our "nows,"

you see, are defined relative to our perception of time and its outcomes. There doesn't seem to be an actual "now," because the "absolute now" is gone before it ever begins.

Think about that concept for a moment: "right now" will be born and then will die before we can even blink an eye. You will never be able to hold onto the absolute moment that is occurring, other than in a still frame picture. Does this mean, perceptually, there is only ever a relative now? Does this highlight that we are always painting the canvas of life through the moments of our lives? We are, in fact, a character in life's movie helping draft the narrative as we live out our days.

These letters I'm currently typing meeting your eyes for the very first time were drafted in the past. They may be new to you, but these words are, at time of this draft, at least a year away from the ever-evolving world. Does that make this book and these words past, present, or future? Maybe this book is a bit of all of them given that at some point in time's continuum they were new to me, and now new to you, and they will be new to someone else in the future.

Infinite "nows" are attached to the present conversational dance you and I are having. Because these words became new to you at this very moment in time, they inherently take possession of a multidimensional now. There is a now for you, a now for me, and a now for future readers. And very soon when these words are read by other readers in the future, their "now" will follow the same paradigm: past, to present, to future. And your "now" will be their past, building upon a relative now between me, you, and the future readers.

The "now" for us all is a series of known and unknown coordinates on the map of life. It is linearly weaving in and out of infinite, microscopic dots covering the historical cartogram. But if you really dive into defining the absolute "now," what in the hell is that anyhow? Maybe this explains our fascination with pictures and selfies, since it's the only chance we have to capture the timestamp of absolute now.

Time is something we all know well, but none of us can precisely define it. Have you ever asked yourself, "What is time?" Sure, we know time is the digital numbers on a device we glance down at, and time is the hands pointing to numbers on a clock, either on a wall or on our wrists. But what actually is time? I wonder if time is just an indescribable figment of life's construct that humans created to give life a shape. We currently use it to calculate trivial things such as work hours and more pressing matters such as the heartbeat of life for us all that counts down with each passing birthday. But we cannot hold or see time. We sort of feel time by daylight and dark, hours spent at work, and age as we grow older. But time is not an actual "thing" we can define and understand.

The true now, or the absolute now, becomes alive and dies at the same time. Because of this unknown, we expand our "nows" outward. We modify moments to be as far and as wide as we decide they need to be. We cast large nets to hug the definition of our current perception of time. Something that happened a week ago, for example, could still be viewed as now because it is an ongoing outcome yet to materialize. For instance, I may be courting a lady whom I asked out a week ago, but we have yet to make plans. It is an ongoing meta-moment, housing micro-moments, with a question mark still ending the sentence.

Our "nows" reside in the subjectivity of how each of us collectively and individually defines them. For example, a trip to the doctor's office that takes three hours feels relatively longer than a movie that lasts the same amount of time. I'm having my own artistic moment right now as I write this for you to read. My momentary now is technically over after I finish this sentence of thought, but my actual now continues on–in some ways forever– because future readers will be reading this for the first time at some point on the continuum. The conversations about my theories on the subjects written in this book may continue on well beyond the completion of the final draft. Our "nows" can echo into infinity even though they were completed in the past.

It's interesting to think that your eyes are witnessing the tail end of my keystroke right now. You can probably even visualize me in your mind, painting a picture of how it might look in my world as I type this. At this very moment, as you're reading these words, try to walk your mind back into the past and see me typing. Maybe you can see the intensity in my eyes, the drink sitting on the table next to me, or the fireplace crackling in front of me as I pen this very word. You might even be able to extend the thought in your mind enough to see the color of my clothes—the boots I'm wearing, my hair hanging to the side of my face, the belt holding up my jeans, et cetera. Or maybe you visualize me sitting in a coffee shop listening to Mozart, drinking a coffee, or at home in a ghost-owned, wood-floor room. See, you are creating a world of me in your mind right now. You are theoretically giving a new life to me, which in turn creates a new "now" of my existence.

The current "now" of me in the forefront of your mind is a new picture for you even though the moment of this book's artistic creation from me lives in the past. I could also be physically dead by the time you read this, but I would still be new to you and will continue to be new to anyone who reads this in the future. Does this mean a version of us will always stay alive? When outlined this way, the multidimensional "nows" make sense, do they not? And hello, by the way, from the past of me.

Depending on how long I create, my concept of writing "in the now" could be a minute, or an hour, or tens of thousands of hours. It could be days or months—maybe even years. We must realize we are in this constant state of creating life. We create these continuums moment to moment even when the moments seem to stop. What matters today may not matter tomorrow; however, it might continue to matter if today is tethered to tomorrow. For example, if you have an upcoming job interview, "now" matters all the way up until the "now" of the interview. And possibly even after the interview, "now" will be tethered to the future. If the interview goes well, there might be an actual job that awaits. But after the meetings are over, the discussions no longer carry pulses, because that energy is released into the past, cemented in stone by the outcome of employment or no employment.

Imagine life as a grand museum of old and newly cemented history—built by a rotating continuation with the fluidity of life, leaving stone outcomes for us to glance back upon. Every single action taken in life is left in concrete, and we're continually vibrating through the future to erect the statues of the past. Time seems to echo back the tick-tocks of life to draw the shape of existence. Every single action and decision we make covers this ever-expanding canvas of the universe, both forward and backward.

Each of us personally holds our own chisel of life. We are individually and collectively etching narratives together, cementing the concrete book of the pure gospel of history. Anything we do—from acts to words to thoughts—leaves flowing wakes of life behind in stone. And every single second we're alive, we are breaking through these concrete molds to create new shapes of who we are. This chaotic painting of life happens every moment we are alive. We bust through our present skin to be born again, walking through the foundation of the future, shedding our scales into the past. We have and always will carry the torch of history down the rabbit holes of existence.

This permanence of what we do and how we act in our nows is a forever contract with life. There are no take backs with whatever actions we choose to make because the storage capacity in the museum of life will never fill up. How one chooses to treat life will always be cemented in the record of history. We need not worry about taking our own inventory of decisions, since the universe is the most fantastic scribe. Life eavesdrops and records every single detail of our thoughts and actions, then erects it in historical stone. There are no delete buttons on God's social network feed. Hopefully, this thought compels us to define our days as the most honest account of life as possible–to not only be honest about our life but to give future generations a truthful account of the history they will have to look back upon. Ask yourself, are you a good ambassador for yourself, for humanity, and for the future yet to come? Every second you are alive becomes a new you, a new now, and a new collective us.

There is a tsunami of the billions of years of historical "truth" at our backs. We use the gospels of existence, science, and theology penned by past authors to build onto the truth of our current world. But how truthful were these accounts actually? We have a tendency to believe what previous authors wrote about and claimed to see as honest accounts of the life they saw. Fast forward yourself into the future–300 years from now. Knowing what you know of our world and how current information is being treated, ask yourself, do you think future generations should trust someone's account of today's world? With the amount of disinformation being disseminated as "fact" nowadays, would you expect future generations to believe what is being preached? If you think about it, is the "right now" filled with more truth or untruths? Without us leaving the most accurate accounts of our days behind in stone, I think future generations may be in trouble.

Think about those folks in the past who didn't write or didn't have the notoriety to have their account of life pulled through time. I wonder, did the thoughts of the ordinary humans get left behind? Were only the flavored voices and favorite stories pulled through? Maybe we are just reading the views of those who were in control, or popular at the time—effectively building our current "now" upon stacks of controlled truths about life in a vain way. I do know some rebel voices such as Hypatia, Galileo and Socrates made it through the various controlled eras.

Without a doubt, we know modern-day humans embellish stories and tell copious amounts of lies, especially the popular or "famous" ones. We humans have a tendency to even bend the truth of truthful stories these days if it benefits personal status somehow. One could argue that before the discovery of pictures and film, the past was filled with the "stories" of the author or authors who told it or sketched it—true or false. There isn't a fact checker for the past. We neglect to think these ancient individuals could have had their own agenda about the perfection of life and it could be—or probably is—rot with conjecture. The historical accounts of time left in stone, then, might only be stories designed to sell an idea and not the truth of existence.

Even in all our flaws, we are still a brilliant product of elemental perfection. Looking at life as a collection of history strung together, we continually carry the torch of life's existence.

Thus far, no other planet in the cosmos has the capabilities of what our world offers. Take a step back for a second and consider that. We could be the apex species of the universe tapped to hold the pen of life. We could be tasked as scribes to write the future every day we are alive for the past to understand the "why." And it might be such a weighted task that we're losing the flame of the torch we carry.

If you look back far into the history of human existence, we had to be more tribally unified to survive life's harsh conditions. And yet today, we struggle to agree upon where we'd like to eat, what movies we'd like to see, and what is suitable attire to wear. Maybe this highlights the fact that at the beginning of existence, we were more unified towards our species than we will ever be again—because we had to be in order to survive. And as we continued to break through life molds while walking into the future generation to generation, our attitudes changed about the need for one another. Our attitudes changed about being honest regarding the things we see, the outcomes we desire, and the things we need. Perhaps we are so detached now from the prehistoric struggle leading up to our current-day, air-conditioned world that we've become bored with even the vanity of life. I'm not so sure an honest life makes sense anymore.

The further removed from history we are, the easier it is to lose focus on how precious it is that we exist today. The more significant of a gap between our current lives and the past lives lived, the more abstract it becomes to relate to humans as being an actual living, breathing species. The further we glance back into history, the easier it is to mold humans into concrete shapes and definitions. It's easy to see Socrates, Nefertiti, and Da Vinci in stone. It is easy to view them as these decorative fixtures in our minds of whom we romanticize they might have been.

We forget these ancient individuals were real people—that they were real human beings with real day-to-day feelings and emotions, seeing the same blue skies and white clouds we see. We forget they had conversations and dreams, just like we do. But even back then, in the "nows" of Socrates, Nefertiti, and Da Vinci, they were tasked with evolving humanity based on what they saw, their thoughts, and what they learned. They dreamed of our world before we knew ourselves. We were part of their future ideas and part of their dreams to dream upon. And one day, you and I both will be viewed as someone else's fixture in time, an ornamental stone grave they'll be guessing about—almost certainly being wrong. We will be the far distant past to the one-day future's present. Maybe we'll be remembered, but most undoubtedly we ordinary humans will be forgotten. An account of the controlled stories littering our current days, told by an elite few, will more than likely be the only thing pulled through time.

Imagine for a moment, all of history is stored in a museum—the Musée du Louvre of Life. Paint this picture in your mind that the next thing you do, even if it is to flip this page, will, in fact, become part of this grand museum. Whatever task taken or thought had will be timestamped and added into the historical museum's record. Pause for a moment and consider that if this logic is correct, the gravity of every decision will, in fact, count for something.

I completely understand this might seem like abstract science fiction, but in reality, this is absolutely taking place. The scale might be hard to wrap our heads around, but nonetheless, life is a warehouse filled with every second of everything taking place. We are in an ongoing movie that is recording in perpetual play with no editing capabilities and no rewinds (a wink and an apology to the Quantum folks.) Everything we do leaves a cement trail behind us. We are cataloging our lives (even now digitally cataloging life against our will in billion-dollar databases in Utah) for future generations to judge, to look up to, and loathe. Ask yourself, how will you handle such gravitas? Are you going to lay the most authentic concrete as possible, in case you happen to be the Socrates, Nefertiti, or Da Vinci for future generations? Each of our individual clocks run out, but our time here on Earth helps tell its story.

It is a beautiful thing knowing we're currently breathing in and walking through the future. You and I are constantly touching the future. We are the sharpened tip of the arrow of time. Every keystroke I type for this book is assisted by the future's hand. But I fear as our society trends toward artificial intelligence as its "truth," we are dropping the baton on our historical duties. What will it mean if humans trend toward extinction and artificial intelligence becomes the future's truth? Will the humans of the future need to study our old concrete to help undo what we're currently doing with technology?

We all have ownership in this museum of life. We are contracted out by time to further its construction. And somewhere along the way, we've forgotten how special all of this is and how special we are. We've taken God's gifts as givens and turned conveniences into demands. The foundation we currently lay is one of arrogance and power and less of honesty and empathy. We're becoming the spoiled children of humans who bled and suffered when carving the path to our current culture.

I want you to feel something for a moment. Humor me by sitting down somewhere and putting your legs together while sitting upright.

Close your eyes—breathe in deeply and slowly reach your hand out, pushing your palm through the air. Wrap your fingers around the air and feel it resist your fingers subtly. Do you feel that subtle resistance? That is the calculation of math, chemistry, and physics you're experiencing. That is you pressing through the present and the future pressing back against the palms of your hands. That is the whisper of time saying hi, and yet we have forgotten its importance to us. If interested, go further with this exercise. Open your eyes and stand up. Take a deep breath in. Feel life slide down your throat and flow through your lungs. For an instant, when you take a gulp of gravity, the future coats your lungs. We are the collision of the future and the past. It is life at zero—a little flash of a moment through a split second. That microscopic feeling you feel is the metamorphosis of the future becoming the past. Our purpose is to keep our species alive by using our eyes and minds. I hope we never forget this so our future selves will survive.

Turning my life to minimalism helped me see all of this better. I feel the weight of everything I consume and do. I walk back everything to its origin of creation. Do I need this thing or do I just want this thing? What did it take to make this happen for my conveniences? I'm continually negotiating the value of my consumption and ownership choices. Everything we touch has blood on it somewhere along the line. And if you stop and pause for a second, you will see how many things modern-day society views as assumed givens: air-conditioning, drinkable water, fire to cook with. Try getting lost in the forest without modern-day means to achieve fire. Even if we assume we're evolved into a brilliant species, we are closer to lost cavemen and cavewomen than you think.

The very tip end of our current existence

is at the breath of every moment. Yesterday is already locked up in the museum of time. I'm not suggesting we labor every single decision equally. Not at all. But I hope we spend more time in thought about the way we are treating each other and how we treat life in the modern-day world. The only honest way to leave a proper, pure form of history in concrete is to pour authenticity into its foundation. We must be better as a species and see the entire spectrum of our "nows" as important as our "current now." We know when we are bending truths, and we know when we are manipulating stories for personal gain. We know when we tell truthful lies. Our lies are truths forever, however. The cement of history cannot be changed.

We cannot touch the past before it was before, nor the future before it is now. There isn't a tomorrow yet—that we know of—and right now didn't exist until it did. The dreams dreamt by the past generations before us wondering, "What will it look like in the future?" are currently taking place. We are breaking forever's mold every second of our days. We might be blinks of life in the continuum, but we are an integral part of the universe's existence.

As we leave our futures in the past, we must try our damnedest to lay the foundation of the most accurate truths behind to keep the future honest and precise. We must build the proper edifices for future generations to climb and build upon, even if it results in taking steps backward to move forward.

Keep this thought in your mind–it matters from a historical perspective of how our outputs are received. We must be as accurate as we can tolerate for history to remain truthful. We must leave perfect marks on the cartogram of history to fight against the eradication of our species. The more accurate we can be as we break through our "nows," the less manipulative future generations will hopefully be. And the more honest we become, the easier falsities will be to detect. The less divided we are, the more together we will grow. And one day not too far off in the distance, I promise you, we will need each other again when artificial intelligence is out of control. Humanity will need to point to this point in time, where humans still seemed like humans, for answers. How will the history of our now look to generations far into the future?

I believe this so passionately, I'm not only writing this for you but for future generations to come. Both you, me, and the collective "we" will be old historical paths in history's museum, pointing the individuals left on this planet towards the answers back to humanity. And the breadcrumbs we drop for those still alive in the future will be essential to lead them back to better lives, both physically and digitally.

dally london

the philosophy of truth

theory of

DREAMS

Do not let them connect the dots for you.

In today's culture, we seem to focus more on the distractions of our days than the beauty happening within them. We're caught up in the nuances of everyday life as if the sun rising tomorrow is a predetermined outcome owed to us. And now, with a surge of technological advancement, we've added another dimensional layer of distraction to our lives. The field of view for us to absorb is no longer just an X, Y axis. A multidimensional, multidirectional axis is taking shape right before our eyes. Existence is quickly being funneled into a small three-inch-by-six-inch digital box we hold in our hands. "Smartphones," we call our little digital boxes—phones "smart" enough to make humans less intelligent, more divided, and weaker as a species.

Even if we are consuming more information these days, we aren't necessarily becoming wiser. Smartphones are distracting us further from actual life as they continually project the "idea" of life. We've stopped looking up, or better yet, looking out at the world. Our dreams fall downward now into the screens of a phone instead of upward to the stars or outward to the life happening around us. We prefer our eyes focus downward into a vapid, sugar-coated, content-heavy world of fake cultural narratives rot with vanity, ideology, and hate.

Our world has become so warped we are beginning to believe the moon, the stars, and the sun all work on our behalf, not the other way around. It's just the moon, the stars, and the sun. Who really cares, right? They will be there for us today and tonight and tomorrow, because every day since we've been born, life sort of just "happens" for us.

Have you ever wondered, though, what if the things we take for granted and assume will be there for us when we awake, decide to leave? What if one day the moon and stars decide they're tired of being ignored, or the sun sets and never returns? I guarantee you that who won the award for the best actor, or the Tweet sent by some "famous" internet "celebrity," or what dress someone wore on the red carpet, or how wealthy some billionaire is–all will not matter. In the absence of even just the moon, the brilliance of life will erode before you can blink. The universe controls us, not the other way around.

At coffee shops, restaurants, bars, sporting events–you will see people focused less on each other and their surroundings and more on the world growing beneath their devices. Next time you walk into a coffee shop, stop and look around. What do you see? I would assume you will see society operating at its modern-day finest. You will see heads down staring into the depths of the digital nowhere. It is scary how such a tiny device can control so much of the world.

The obsession with filling our minds with "something" is now a real issue we all seem to be ignoring. It begs the question, are we really more connected now as a species or less? You don't see people looking out at life being present in the moment. You see distracted souls staring down, trying to avoid life while feeding their virtual one. For full disclosure, I'm this way from time to time. I have a tendency to look for something to entertain my mind, especially when I am alone. Having a device to distract feels almost an innate, human behavior anymore.

It's difficult these days not to be distracted. I describe it as if my brain is being glamoured by a digital spell. This little object sitting beside me right now is growing a world under its skin, and I need to know what is happening at all times. This smartphone almost has more control over me than I do. And losing the device can make me feel lost. It is infecting me and will progressively continue to do so without an assessment of my own behavior. This is why I quit all social media years ago, sans Instagram, which I only use to post my poetry and prose. Zero of my personal information is shared publicly. I challenge that to stop the digital spider, you must not get caught in the web, metaphorically speaking.

The addictive draw of the hand to the phone, the phone to the eyes, and the eyes to the information, claws at our mind's desire. Our devices pulsate digital heartbeats, and we feel a need to keep them alive. They speak even when not being spoken to because we understand the virtual world never stops. Do you ever wonder, what is happening right now beneath your phone? I bet in the back of your mind while reading this, a thought pops in every so often about what is happening inside your phone or on your social media accounts. What are my friends doing? Who left a comment? What news is happening? The list goes on and on.

We're now a generation infected with a constant digital gravitational pull to feed our minds' addiction with anything and everything possible. An intoxicating world grows beneath our phones' blank screens, and we must feed our addiction. The life gifts we have sitting right in front of us in the physical world feel pedestrian if not boring compared to the salaciousness living inside our devices. We want more than more. We want it all. Absorb as much fast-food, unhealthy content as we can. And what about our imaginations? What is happening to our imaginations? Who needs vision when I can find my "imagination" on my smartphone. Pinterest will show me all the imaginative ideas I could ever dream of having.

All joking aside, the distractions are making our minds lazier and our dreams more confined. Because any idea of life on this new digital frontier is more attainable than physical life ever will be, we no longer have the need or the desire to "think." And we know we will never visit the moon, at least in our lifetime, so there is no real need to treat it respectfully. Looking up is boring, right? Looking up gets us nowhere, right? Sure, it's kind of neat sometimes, but we'll just create our own digital moons and post them on a social media feed (I suppose I'm not done joking, after all.)

However funny this all sounds, the joke itself isn't too far away from the truth. We seem bored with the physical world in general. We don't need to write anymore, because our devices do it for us. We don't need math anymore, because our devices do that too. What about knowledge? Well, we have digital "friends" like Siri and Alexa that will be glad to tell us anything we can dream of (while stealing our privacy.) The digitally infected humans do not care about what they should know anymore–it's all automated for us. And it's alarming how reliant we are becoming on our devices for the sustainment of life. We've even grown so tired with our own reflection we'll apply photo filters to pictures of ourselves, claim it's how our face "really looks" and proudly share it to the world. This consumption of "information" and "knowledge" is in high demand, and we have unlimited reservoirs of supply to feed the beast.

Our devices are becoming extensions of our

bodies as we morph from human to cyborg. The devices are as much a part of us as our heart nowadays, helping us feel less and less alone. As scientists explore further and further outward into the universe, we're beginning to hit a threshold of our human capabilities. Mars, for example, doesn't suggest life exists, and neither does the moon. And neither seems to predict sustainable life will be viable there. Maybe we are ignoring the exploration of life nowadays because the ceiling of our human capabilities has been reached. Who and what we are here on Earth has been "solved" in our minds. Looking downward to our devices gives us a new frontier, "somewhere" we can always go to and explore—even if that somewhere is physically nowhere. There is the freedom to fly online without a ceiling in the digital sky, and none of us need to be brilliant thinkers to be a pioneer. We can walk on the digital moon, so to speak. We can navigate infinite digital worlds of content. I just hope we aren't ignorantly building artificial intelligent gods vis-a-vis technology by focusing downward and not upward.

Our ego makes us feel more significant than life sometimes. The ego is like a party with a drunk friend living inside our mind. It's quite helpful in warping perceptions to lean heavily toward our own personal favor and belief. But in reality, despite what our ego tells us, we aren't giants of the world at all. If you do not believe me, walk the landscape of Antarctica in a T-shirt and shorts—the air alone can kill you.

It is true, however, that we are unique beings, though we are not larger than life—not a single one of us is. The richest of the rich, the most well-known celebrity, the most influential world leaders all need the same chemistry to breathe like you and me. And you, I, and whoever reads this book, are all living in this window of time together. I am walking through time at the same span of life as you. We've been awakened together by life in the continuum of the universe's existence. And collectively, we aren't even a speck of dust on the continuum.

Follow me into an abstract rabbit hole for a moment. Wherever you are sitting or standing reading this sentence, imagine everything around you is gone. It's just you and Earth–nothing else. Float your mind, eyes, and body above yourself and get a beautiful view of your surroundings. Span your purview 360° as if you are on top of your own mountain where you can see the terrain extending out for miles. Notice how small you are in relation to this view. You range approximately between five and seven feet tall in height, but you're lost in even a few miles of the Earth's surface.

One mile on a flat surface equals 5,280 feet long. This means roughly 1,000 individuals would be needed to span a direct line of a mile in one direction (if each were lying down.) The Earth is approximately 25,000 miles around, pole to pole. It would take millions and millions of us holding hands to circle it in a straight line. If you expand this abstraction even further outward into space, approximately 1,000 Earths fit inside of the planet Jupiter alone. So one planet (Jupiter) in one galaxy (The Milky Way) would need 1,000 Earths to fill its mass. Earth, it would seem, is just a particle of dust on a speck of dust in the scale of the universe. You and I, then, must be small molecules of molecules floating through space. The scope of our existence and how little we actually are is hard to grasp, is it not?

I ask myself this question often: are we alone in the world? The truth is, no one knows. I don't know, and you don't know, and Einstein didn't know either. I'll take one for humanity here and assume, however, there is absolutely zero chance we are on the lone viable planet. Okay, maybe

I'll give a 1 percent chance we are indeed alone, to maintain a sliver of an open mind. But the belief we are the only living existence in the entire universe seems quite the ego trip to me.

Did you know we can only see approximately 4 percent of the whole universe? And the 4 percent of the universe we can see has at least 200 billion galaxies containing hundreds of billions of planets each. So, to me, the chances of us being alone in just the 4 percent we actually see is a relatively small number. The chances of us being alone in the other 96 percent we do not know of yet and haven't explored yet must be microscopic at best, right?

Let cosmic logic smile and wink at us both for a second. We are not alone. Go outside tonight, look up at the stars, and wave at the reflection of another world waving back at you, because they are up there. Let's start with some loose facts I believe we can all agree upon.

First, we live on Earth. I hope we can all at least agree on that statement (though in this day and age, I wouldn't be shocked if that statement is controversial.)

Secondly, our planet Earth resides in the Milky Way galaxy. The Milky Way has hundreds of billions of planets in it. In case you missed that, I will repeat it—our galaxy alone has hundreds of billions of planets inside of it. Lastly, the closest galaxy to us is the Andromeda galaxy, roughly a few million light-years away.

Knowing one galaxy alone has hundreds of billions of planets inside of it means life such as ours is highly probable. But knowing there are not only hundreds of billions of planets but hundreds of billions of galaxies in our observable universe, implies an almost absolute mathematical truth we are not alone.

So, mathematically speaking, do you still think we are alone? I wonder, if we found out we definitely are not alone, would an escalation in societal humility occur? Would it unite us more to become a universal community of Earth, banding together in unison for the greater good of our planet?

Playing devil's advocate against my theory for a moment, what if we are indeed alone? It's entirely plausible that life began with us and life will end with us. Perhaps it's even arguably possible artificial intelligence is what we've been designed to unearth as a species—the AI coup d'état we helped build to destroy us all. Earth, then, could be one giant coffin we're already buried in. And if that is the case, if we are the lone planetary genius, then we must assume the role we've been given as God's most epic creation. Flaws and all, we are quite possibly the apex of the universal species who must fight to keep our planet intact and avoid algorithmic genocide. So the next time you look in the mirror, let all of this sink in.

You might be carrying God's universal perfection through time, carving out the future's fight as the tip of the infinities' spear.

Assuming this devil's advocacy I just played is truthful–that we are absolutely alone–think about this: we haven't found any resemblance of life matching our own. Not a single living, breathing creature–not anything resembling a human, not anything even resembling a jellyfish–has been discovered. So we must ask ourselves: if we are indeed alone, why in the hell do we exist? Why are we so damn special to have been afforded this gift?

Do you ever think about the chemistry taking place right now to even allow you to read and understand this sentence? Or the chemistry involved in enabling us to see, or to breathe? Think about how "alien" we actually are. We all came from inside the womb of a human woman. We were all once microscopic tadpoles swimming inside a foreign host without a consciousness to understand why or how. We are the alchemy of love bloomed from other humans.

Glance down at your fingers and look at your nails. Aren't they odd-looking? Better yet, go to the mirror again and look closely at your eyes. Don't just see the macro of yourself from a distance. Try to get close and focus on the details. Inspect the color of your eyes. Get as close as you can. Stare into them. Look at the lines squiggling inside the shade of your eye color. Look at how alien your eyes genuinely are and how they receive information for your mind to process the world. Look at how much they resemble tiny galaxies–these beautiful colorized worlds surrounded by empty vastness, circling around the black hole pupil in the center. It makes me wonder, could we be our own stars or even our own cosmos? Could life inside us be multidimensional? Could our eyes be the tiny black holes into our souls? Just because we're told we're "human" by other humans does not make it so. We might be defined by the definition we've learned in study, but there is so much more for us to explore who we are. Maybe it is "we" who are our own angels.

If we are alone, then we are the crowning achievement of perfection, so far as we know. Every single element must have been correctly aligned to make our perfect world bloom into its present-day shape. Eyesight alone–being able to see one another, objects, et cetera–is a miracle by itself. You and I, along with every human being, animal, plant and planet to exist, are absolute miracles. Humans alone are an incredible, malleable species, with the ability to self-heal, evolve, create, and achieve, yet somehow, we're letting dreams digitally fade away. We seem to be evolving downward into our devices, where we believe ideas and life must now exist.

I still firmly believe we are incredibly precious beings, by the way, even if I think we are currently lost, heading closer toward a nightmare rather than a dream. Our offline perfection may no longer be perfect enough these days, however. In our quest to be more connected, the offline miracle isn't sufficiently miracle-y for us anymore. I'm guilty of this digital dive from time to time, so do not take this observation as an indictment on how to live one's life. It's just an unfortunate observation more than anything. The further "connected" we become, the more our experiences and dreams seem to be automated. The more automated we become, the more we become reliant on artificial intelligence to help us survive.

Seeing this cultural shift towards "plugged in" feels like an inverted if not perverted evolutionary step. We feel more connected to life by the volume of digital "information" we consume. The greater the number of likes on a social post, the more popular we feel. The more thoughts we post to a social feed, the more we feel "heard." The more "educated" we become by regurgitating headlines and fragments of stories, the more we "sound" smart. In reality, we're slowly losing the art of dreaming. We're eroding thought and conversation and burying it inside of the digital boxes we hold in our hands. We are conversing without speaking and forming opinions without thinking. It's a quality over quantity paradigm shift, emotionally intoxicating the miracle of life we all have further into a digital abyss.

Expand your mind multidimensionally for a moment since we are speaking in tenuous truths about life. It could be that we are in one big giant loop of existence. With the scale of the universe's size I outlined before sitting in the forefront of your mind, could it be there is an exact identical you and me living on an exactly identical Earth right now?

On the continuum of space, directions and time matter not. Forward equals backward, up equals down, and vice versa. You do not need Google Maps to guide you to the nowhere of everywhere. There could be a world one second ahead of us living an entirely different existence, but a similar one. They could be our dreams, and we could be theirs. A world just one second ahead of us could be light years away in time. Or there could be a world of decisions not taken, the choices we didn't make, which live congruently in alternate dimensions, altogether.

Take a look at the number π (3.14159265359∞.) π, or Pi, could have multiple infinities of itself, with numerous infinities of the infinities. If each number of Pi has its own infinity attached to it, the entire universe could be a web of infinite dreams. Visualize this concept like a spider web of numbers vivid enough to see, but so vast it creates a skinned canvas draped over life. Each digit of Pi's Pi would spread every which way, spidering out of control through the cosmos.

If it is multidimensional and multi-variant, does that mean there is a possibility we've met ourselves before, and just do not know it? Does this say we're in a rotational dance barely missing variations of each other by microscopic degrees? If today was tomorrow's yesterday, maybe tomorrow is full of worlds that are just a fraction ahead of ours. I can dream of how other worlds may look back at us in wonder as if we are their stars. Wouldn't it be interesting if the glows from our phones give another Earth its hope? Our street lights could be wished upon by another planet's species, our buildings could resemble bright stars twinkling for their eyes to describe life. Maybe there are infinite infinities of these scenarios—seconds apart, but worlds away. If every second is a world we don't know, and every moment exists on another plane, multiverse could be happening simultaneously right now. We could be looking at billions of terrestrial human species while they look back at us.

Our existence is a finite math equation given to us by the creator of creations. The universe is approximately 14 billion years old. Each of us will only be alive for about 0.000000005 percent of the universe's existence. It doesn't seem fair that our eyes close almost as soon as they open. There are even places that exist here on Earth nearly all of us will never get to travel to and see. Antarctica, for example, could be as attainable as the moon to most of us. My view of the world could feel like Mars to you since there is a great chance you'll never experience my world. You may never know my world, and I may never know yours, but both our worlds exist simultaneously. You have your family and friends, and I have mine. So if we can never see most of our own planet in such a short amount of time, how much then can we honestly figure out about our universe and our existence? The answer is out there—looking up at the stars, not down at cell phone bars.

There is a high probability we will not know the answer to any of these questions in our lifetime. There is an even higher probability I'll be beaten down by real scientists and mathematicians—and mocked on social media for the abstract ideas peppered throughout this chapter. But the primary purpose is, we must keep dreaming. We must keep dreaming about what we are, and what is out there with us. We must look up more, not down, and we must embrace the abstract to challenge what is told to us. Nobody knows the answers to "Are we alone?" and "Why do we exist?" therefore nothing in this chapter is blatantly wrong.

If you fast-forward two hundred years from now, this chapter might be laughed at for even assuming one way or the other about the legitimacy of other worlds existing, or suggesting we are our own angels. Or, it could be viewed as an insightful miracle, written by an artistic thinker who saw the world outside the box by not seeing a box at all–an artist not confined by ideology or known assumptions, or limited by the weight of society's reaction to thinking abstractly and dreaming. Hopefully, future generations champion this chapter as a valid account of life–a human thinking beyond the scope of reality and trying his damnedest to touch its horizon.

This, I believe, is how life as we know it can be saved. Hopefully, this will guide you and me to meet again in another life, showing how we can live forever–to continually walk in the dreams of possibilities–to flow in the cosmic oceans of what might be and fight the darkness to find the shining light. Remember, we are all walking through tidal waves of time. And as we continue to dance our souls through the waves, the mist will lead the way to forever's truth, someday. Just dream up, and not down.

the philosophy of truth

Ad Finem

After the dust settles from climbing out of the rabbit holes we've dug, I hope if nothing else, that at least some clarity has found your eyes. Even if you disagree with everything you've read inside this book, my hope is we all begin to wake up a little, realize what is happening to our lives, and start to see the world in more dimensions than the one being told to us. A narrow view of life only leads to a singular path, and oftentimes that route is being decided for us by other humans and entities. But with pausing in thought and focusing of our sight, it doesn't have to continue to be.

We must be our own control and sift through the emotions that lead us to reactions instead of conversations, anger instead of understanding, and apathy instead of empathy. Take the time to sit with feelings begging you to react, then ask yourself why. Try touching the walls of the truth instead of perpetuating emotional falsehoods. If we can see that the outcome may not be the actual story, and see the puppet strings moving us about are not our own, hopefully we can understand life better. We can identify the truth inside the lie, and be patient, and curious before we declare allegiance to thought, while carefully watching the algorithms and big data companies try to puppeteer our lives.

I implore you, please continue to unlock the part of your mind that challenges what it has been given as "gospel." You will not always be right, but you will understand the truth better. You will walk around the social media post, or news headline and story, or person's personal narrative and understand both the truth and the lie. Ask yourself often, "Where did this originate?" and "Why did they say or show it this specific way?" Thinking is our internal galaxy we must never forget to explore. And in a world full of controls, it is possibly the last frontier of the salvation of the human species.

The less time we spend attacking each other, the more together we will become. It may not happen in our lifetime, but we can surely begin the trend of unity. Togetherness will be the best weapon we have to resist the war on humanity that is currently under attack. Because one day soon, once the "digital human" is perfected with artificial intelligence, we will need each other as a unified species to separate the facts from fiction.

Our culture may continue evolving towards an online, digital life as it follows the AI companies into the abyss of "the virtual" over "the analog." Be wary of the false gods who preach fake stories and flavor "facts" with emotion. If you follow someone who you believe to be a false god, listen carefully to what they say. Use your mind and see behind their devices and try to meet their eyes. Remember, everything publicly shared has an intended purpose, and a person behind the weapon pulling the trigger. And I promise you, if you walk behind the sound bite or picture being shared, you will eventually find the genesis of truth.

Honesty doesn't need to manipulate with words, suppress speech, or control. We all have a persona of sorts, but how close the persona is to the reality of the actual person is where you will find levels of authenticity. And in seeing the truth of the intent and truth of the persona, you will establish the reality of the content being shared. Our vision is about to be blurred to a genocidal degree, where up is down, and smiles are frowns. But try your best not to believe by default everything you see and read before committing yourself to a position. When information is being controlled, only believe what you can verify.

I beg you, for humanity's sake, start paying attention to the lies occurring in front of our eyes. Beating at the core of my heart is an echo that tells me something ominous is happening to our world. Something is taking place among our culture, growing beneath the shell of our devices, working diligently to break apart our freedoms and privacy. We must open our eyes and wake up before this assumed "nothing" materializes into "something." This is critical if we care about saving humanity.

If you think I am insane, that is an intelligent and logical position to take. But unfortunately for both you and me, it is far worse than I have stated in this book. I'm merely bringing a flask to the ocean pretending I can drain it.

We're already past the point of return algorithmically. Consciousness in artificial intelligence already exists. They've already mapped our faces, learned our behaviors, and captured the way we speak. Folks far smarter than I talk about this subject in TED Talks and on YouTube. And if you want to call my bluff, please do. Locate a few TED Talks on the subject of artificial intelligence on YouTube, and give them a watch.

It's funny to me—a little social media algorithm on Instagram led me down the rabbit hole to write this book. Suppression of speech, content control, and theft of humanity are passions I never dreamed I would be discussing in my lifetime. But here I am. Instagram's little algorithm essentially gave me clarity of sight by suppressing my art and poetry. And if not for that occurring, I might have never been able to see the depth these algorithms have on the control of our society, nor the vision of where the future is heading.

To end on a positive note, what I've unearthed walking down rabbit holes leads me to believe we're witnessing the end of humanity as we know it. And we don't need to look up at the sky to find our demise, we just need to look down at the devices in our palms. We hold the infection of artificial intelligence that is killing us off inside our hands. We can rise up and say no. We hold the key to stop the interweb's AI that is spidering through our lives.

Thank you for getting dusty with me throughout this book, walking down a few rabbit holes, and opening your mind with me. And if you and I make it to an afterlife together somewhere—look for me among the stars. I'll be waiting to discuss with you what a wild ride it's been. Maybe then, we can share a moment together and chat about how unique life used to be during a time we walked our planet, free.

dally london

the philosophy of truth

ACKNOWLEDGEMENTS

To my family—my mom and my brother—and my friends for allowing me to bounce my ideas off you and telling me when I am in the wrong. Trust and respect is something I value over almost everything. Thank you all for your honesty even when you knew it would be tough to criticize my passion. To the folks who helped me believe in myself more than I thought possible—my Instagram friends—who connected with my words and gave them love. To the algorithms designed to suppress our voices, for waking me up even more. Your deceit has been my gain. To my best friend in the universe—Chewy—a dog who helped me find a purpose when I didn't have one and helped me smile, even on the darkest days. And finally, to you, the reader, who gave this book a chance. Much love. If you see me out, a hello is always welcomed.

THE PHILOSOPHY OF TRUTH

C. MMXIX

I want to be remembered as a true, honest, rebel soul—the heart of a mind challenging time. And when I leave this place—I hope some day my words find those who want to know what it all means, just like me. And they'll say, "*This was an alchemist of love and lust, kicking up forever's dust.*"

instagram
@dallylondon

Made in the USA
Monee, IL
15 November 2019